The Illustrated Encyclopedia of
AVIATION

Volume
20

Wings Prelims

Reference edition published 1979

Reference edition © 1979 Marshall Cavendish Limited
© Orbis Publishing Limited 1977

Printed in Great Britain

Bound in the United States

Library of Congress Cataloging in Publication Data
Main entry under title:

The Illustrated encyclopedia of aviation.

First published in 1977 under title: Wings.
Includes index.
1. Aeronautics—History. I. Robinson, Anthony,
1947—
TL515.144 1979   629.13'009   78—12408
ISBN 0—85685—318—6 (set)
ISBN 0—85685—593—6 (vol 20)

Picture Acknowledgements

Cover: M. Jerram—2281: Musée de l'Air; E.F. Cheeseman—2282: E.F. Cheeseman—2283: IWM—2284: US Air Force Art Collection—2285: J. Goulding—2286: IWM; E.F. Cheeseman—2287: A. Imrie—2288: A. Imrie; H.J. Nowarra via E.F. Cheeseman—2299-89: A. Imrie—2289: E.F. Cheeseman—2290: API; US Navy—2291-92: Vought Corporation—2293: US Navy; Vought Corporation—2295: Popperfoto; US Navy—2296: P. Endsleigh Castle—2296-97: M. Jerram—2297: US Navy; P. Kilduff—2298: Vought Corporation; P.R. March—2299: P. Endsleigh Castle—2301: M. Jerram—2302: M. Jerram; Vultee—2303: P. Endsleigh Castle—2304: Convair—2305: USAF—2306: Deutsches Museum, Munich—2307: IWM; Australian War Memorial—2308: IWM—2309-10: M. Jerram—2311: M. Jerram; IWM—2312-15: IWM—2316-17: IWM; MAP: Elias/Miller/Robinson Collection—2318: Orbis: South-Eastern Newspapers Ltd—2319: Bundesarchiv—2320: South-Eastern Newspapers Ltd—2321: IWM—2322-23: Keystone—2323: MoD—2324: D. James—2324-25: J. Goulding—2325: Westland—2326-27: Westland—2327: Westland—2328: IWM; Westland; API—2330-31: M.J. Hooks—2331: P.R. March—2332: D.J. Kingston; P.R. March; Westland—2334: P.R. March—2334-35: P.R. March—2336: P.R. March—2336-37: P. Endsleigh Castle—2337: D.J. Kingston—2338: Radio Times Hulton Picture Library—2339: Radio Times Hulton Picture Library; US Signal Corps—2340: Flight—2342: Science Museum/A. Hornak; IWM—2343: Science Museum/A. Hornak; Radio Times Picture Library—2344: P. Endsleigh Castle—2345: C. Shores; Keystone; B. Hiam/O. Siirila; Robert Hunt Picture Library—2346: P. Endsleigh Castle; C. Shores—2347: Keystone; Novosti; J.P. Alexander via C. Shores; Keystone—2348: Keystone; Orbis—2349: Science Museum—2350-51: P. Sarson/A. Bryan—2351: Wright Brothers National Memorial—2352: US National Archives—2353: US National Archives; Science Museum; Wright Brothers National Memorial—2354-55: Flight—2355: J.P. Alexander—2356: IWM—2356-57: P. Endsleigh Castle—2358: J.P. Alexander; API—2359: P.R. March; J.P. Alexander—2360: J.P. Alexander; US Navy—2361: J. Goulding; M.B. Passingham—2362: US Navy; J.P. Alexander—2363: D.J. Kingston—2364: Popperfoto—2365: USAF—2366: Popperfoto—2367: M.B. Passingham; P. Endsleigh Castle—2370: Popperfoto—2370-71: Popperfoto—2371: Keystone—2372: Popperfoto—2372-73: Keystone—2374: Popperfoto; Keystone—2375: IWM—2376: IWM—2376-77: J. Goulding—2377: IWM—2378-80: M.J. Hooks

The Illustrated Encyclopedia of
AVIATION

Marshall Cavendish New York & London

Contents

Ten Thousand Kites

The company established by Gabriel and Charles Voisin in 1905 produced over 10,000 aircraft by 1918

Born at Belleville-sur-Saône on 5 February 1880, Gabriel Voisin was educated at the Lycée Ampère de Lyon and later at the Ecole des Beaux-Arts. At the age of 17 he showed an early interest in aviation, building a Hargrave-type boxkite, but his first job was as a trainee architect. However, he was not destined for a career in architecture, and soon became involved in attempts to construct a practical ornithopter (flapping wing aircraft), which was powered by an electric battery. His first real steps towards an aviation career came after the completion of military service, when on the recommendation of Captain Ferber he secured a post with the Etablissement Aérostatique at Chalais-Meudon, near Paris. It was the director of this headquarters of military ballooning, Colonel Renard, who put him in touch with the wealthy lawyer-sportsman Ernest Archdeacon of the Aéro Club de France.

The Wrights' influence

Aviation in Europe – largely moribund since the death of Otto Lilienthal in 1896 – had been given a boost early in 1903 through a lecture to the Aéro Club by Octave Chanute, describing the design, construction and successful testing of the Wright brothers' third glider. Archdeacon ordered a glider of his own, based on this, which was to provide the foundation for a number of subsequent early French aircraft. Voisin was involved to a considerable extent in the glider's design, manufacture and finally in April 1904 its test-flying.

Archdeacon commissioned a second glider in 1905, retaining the Wright-type forward elevator, but adding a fin and tailplane at the rear. After this had been tested, Voisin applied the Hargrave boxkite concept to the wings and the rear tail unit. In this form it was further tested on the River Seine, towed by a Tellier motor-boat, and made brief flights in June and July of that year. This, and a similar (but less successful) float glider built in association with Louis Blériot – the two combined forces in July 1905 to run the Ateliers d'Aviation Edouard Surcouf, Blériot et Voisin at Billancourt – can be considered the first practical application of the Hargrave boxkite.

In 1905, Gabriel and his brother Charles established at Billancourt a new company known as Appareils d'Aviation Les Frères Voisin, which was the first true commercial manufacturer of aeroplanes on the European continent. The first powered aeroplane produced by this company was the elliptical-wing Blériot III floatplane, powered by a 24 hp Antoinette engine. It was tested at the end of May from the Lac d'Enghien and again in October after conversion to the Blériot IV, but on neither occasion did this machine manage to rise from the water. Voisin had to wait until 1907 before achieving his first successful powered aeroplane. This was known at the time as the Delagrange No 1, its purchaser being Léon Delagrange, and was the second Voisin design, an earlier one built for Henry Kapferer having failed to fly.

Powered by a 50 hp Antoinette engine driving a pusher propeller, Voisin's Delagrange 1 set a basic pattern for Voisin products which lasted over the next four years with

comparatively little change. Reverting to the basic box-kite formula for both the wings and the rear tail unit (though without side-curtains on the wing cellule), it carried a Wright-type biplane frontal elevator, but had no form of lateral control, as neither ailerons nor wing-warping was fitted. Wingspan of the aircraft was 10 m (32 ft 9¾ in) and it weighed 450 kg (992 lb). At Bagatelle (the site of Santos-Dumont's first successful flight in Europe late the previous year) it made half a dozen short flights in March and April 1907, but none of these was longer than 60 m (200 ft). Modified and fitted with floats shortly afterwards, it too was taken to the Lac d'Enghien, only to fail in all attempts to take off. With a wheeled landing gear, and fitting a single central rudder instead of the original pair, Delagrange succeeded in making a 500 m (1,640 ft) flight on 3 November that year, but he crashed at the end of it and wrote off the aircraft.

Above: distinctive features of the early Voisin biplanes were the boxkite wing and tail, which resulted in a stable aeroplane. However, lateral control was poor. Below: Voisin 'chicken coops' were the main French reconnaissance aircraft at the outbreak of World War I. A captured example is pictured under guard

Unchanging design formula

The third powered aircraft to be ordered from Voisin Frères was destined to assume a more important place in aviation history. On 1 June 1907, the Voisins were asked by Henry Farman to build him an aeroplane very similar to that produced for Delagrange. This, too, had a single rear rudder and a slightly increased wingspan. After a few early tests in October, it underwent two significant changes: the wings were re-rigged to give them dihedral–absent on earlier Voisins–and the biplane frontal elevator was replaced by a single surface. The improvements proved immediately effective: lateral stability was improved, turning became easier, and on 9 November it became the first aeroplane of non-Wright design to remain airborne for more than one minute. It was also the first one-kilometre closed-circuit flight to be made in Europe, but since no official observers were present Farman was obliged to repeat his performance at Issy on 13 January 1908 in order to claim the prize of 50,000 francs which had been offered for such a feat.

A second biplane was built for Delagrange, possibly using some of the wreckage from the first machine and incorporating modifications similar to those introduced by Farman. This aeroplane was flown extensively in France and Italy during the first half of 1908, eventually achieving a flight of 14 km ($8\frac{3}{4}$ miles) at Milan on 23 June. Meanwhile, Farman had been making history with his Voisin, after introducing various modifications which transformed the basic Voisin design virtually out of all recognition.

Voisin Frères meanwhile appeared content to continue with the basic boxkite wing and tail formula largely unchanged. It provided a safe and stable aeroplane, although the amount of lateral control which could be exercised was still relatively small. But, even though it was unprogressive in design, it still represented the only near-practical biplane generally available in Europe, the customers were apparently satisfied and orders continued to come in. The great air meeting at Reims in August 1909 saw seven Voisin biplanes among the aircraft entered for various events. By the end of that year nearly 20 of them had been built for various customers, and several more

which Voisin acquired a licence to produce the current type of two-seat Wright biplane in France. The Goupy I, a triplane designed by Ambroise Goupy, was built for him by the Voisins in 1908. It was, however, an unsuccessful design, and it is noteworthy that for his successful Goupy II, Goupy turned to a biplane of much different appearance and had it built by Blériot.

Both the Goupy designs featured tractor-propeller layouts, and Voisin Frères produced a tractor version of their standard boxkite biplane in the autumn of 1909. It was not a success, however, and production of the standard pusher type continued to be the main concern of the company through 1909–10. Apart from minor variations – for example in the landing gear – to suit individual customers' requirements, the 1909 Voisin specification standardised on wings of 10m (32ft 9¾in) span and 40sq m (430·5sq ft) total area and a length of 12m (39ft 4½in). In a typical example a 50hp Antoinette eight-cylinder engine was fitted, giving a take-off weight of 600kg (1,323lb) and a top speed of some 55km/h (34mph). Although slow to accept the inevitable, in 1910 Voisin at last began to evolve developed versions which dispensed with the forward elevator altogether and which introduced lateral control by means of ailerons.

Military orders

In 1911 there appeared a curious canard or tail-first design, its configuration recalling that of Alberto Santos-Dumont's 14-bis of 1906. Initially, it had a conventional wheeled landing gear, but during the summer of 1911 it was modified into an amphibian by the addition of two pairs of floats designed by the pioneer of waterborne flight, Henri Fabre. In early August it was flown by Colliex from Issy-les-Moulineaux, alighted on the Seine, took off again and returned to Issy. As first built, this aircraft had an open-framework fuselage, equal-span wings fitted with double ailerons and a single pair of side-curtains outboard, a square rudder at the front and a 70hp Gnome rotary engine. A developed version, with a covered fuselage and a more powerful Gnome engine, appeared in 1912 and was the first aeroplane to be ordered by the French Marine Nationale. Twelve similar aircraft were ordered by the Aviation Militaire at the end of 1912, and by the outbreak of World War I these were in service with the first two Voisin *escadrilles*, V14 and V21.

After this, almost all the aircraft produced by Voisin were to military or naval contracts. As early as October 1910 the company had displayed, at the Salon de l'Aéronautique in Paris, one of its standard boxkite biplanes fitted with a quick-firing gun mounted in front of the pilot. This proved to be one of the first 'gunbus' applications of an aeroplane to appear anywhere in the world: the Vickers Type 18 'Destroyer', which led to the celebrated FB5 Gunbus of World War I did not appear until three years later. By the end of the war, total output of the company – by then without Charles Voisin, who had been killed in a motoring accident in September 1912 – is claimed to have reached 10,400 aircraft, including co-production of the designs of other companies; this figure prompted the title of Gabriel Voisin's controversial autobiography, *Les 10,000 Cerf-Volants* (The Ten Thousand Kites).

The Voisin biplanes which made up the bulk of production during the war years were quite different in

Above left: a Voisin Type 3 serving with the Royal Naval Air Service.
Left: the basic Voisin airframe could be adapted to take a wide variety of engines, a 150hp Salmson being illustrated.
Above: the nacelle of a Voisin Type 8 night bomber, which entered French service towards the end of 1916

were under construction. They were powered by a wide variety of contemporary engines between 50 and 60hp, including the ENV, Gnome, Gobron, Itala, Renault, Vivinus and Wolesley. The aircraft built for the celebrated French pilot Louis Paulhan, which was one of the competitors in the Easter 1909 meeting at Monaco, was probably the first aeroplane to have flown under the power of the Gnome rotary engine developed by the brothers Laurent and Louis Séguin.

Another early Voisin, first flown on 7 March 1909, was built for the British pilot J. T. C. Moore-Brabazon (later Lord Brabazon of Tara) and was named *Bird of Passage*. This machine had actually been ordered by Henry Farman, but Voisin, for reasons best known to himself, decided to sell it instead to Moore-Brabazon, who did not know of Farman's order. Farman, incensed by this unprofessional and discourteous act, cancelled his order and decided instead to set up his own factory.

An added source of business for the Voisin company followed Wilbur Wright's visit to Europe in 1908–9, during

Left: a departure from standard Voisin practice was an experimental night bomber, which was powered by four 220hp Hispano Suiza engines mounted in tandem

design from the unspectacular boxkites of 1909–10. The biplane wings were of open-cellule configuration, generally with large ailerons protruding from the trailing-edges, while the fuselage consisted of a short central nacelle containing the crew and the rear-mounted pusher engine. The simple cruciform tail unit was carried on openwork booms attached to the wing spars and a tricycle-type landing gear was fitted, with single or twin wheels under the nose. Despite their apparently frail appearance, the Voisin 'chicken coops', as they became known, were sturdily built and proved both battle-worthy and weatherworthy throughout the major part of the war. With their steel and wood airframes and their ability to accept a wide variety of engines of different type and power, they proved surprisingly versatile and formed the backbone of the French bomber and reconnaissance squadrons before and during the early years of the war.

Widespread service

The military designation Voisin 1 was applied to a two-seat biplane with the company title Type L, which was powered by a 70hp Gnome engine and first appeared in early 1914. This type, together with the generally similar Voisin 2 (80hp Le Rhône rotary) was in service before August 1914 with four *escadrilles* of the Aviation Militaire, and in the early months of the war they were used on the Western Front as artillery observation aircraft. In November 1914 they began to be employed for daylight bombing attacks, with about 60kg (132lb) of bombs carried inside or hung on the outside of the central nacelle and released by the observer.

The pre-war Voisin 3, or Type LA, flew for the first times in February 1914; this differed from its stablemates in having unequal-span wings and a more powerful engine, the 120hp Salmson (Canton-Unné) 9M nine-cylinder radial. In the two-seat crew arrangement the observer, who sat in the front cockpit, was provided with a Hotchkiss machine gun, and on 5 October 1914 the gun of Voisin 3

No 89 claimed the first enemy aircraft to be shot down by a French aircrew. Like the earlier models, the Voisin 3 was used at first as a day bomber, but from September 1915 was transferred to night operations. The most widely built type of Voisin bomber, a total of 2,162 was produced in France by Voisin and other companies, including some 800 for the Aviation Militaire, the Marine Nationale, and one *escadrille* of the Belgian Aviation Militaire; 1,200 others were supplied to the Imperial Russian Air Service. A further 112 Voisin 3s, powered by Fiat, Isotta-Fraschini or Renault engines, were produced under licence in Italy by the Società Italiana Transaerea during 1915–16 and served with five *squadriglie* of the Corpo Aeronautica Militare. In Britain, Savage's Ltd built a batch of 50 for the Royal Flying Corps, which also purchased about two dozen more locally in France; the Royal Naval Air Service operated about 30 French-built Voisin 3s.

Later-production French Voisin 3s were of a version designated Type LA.S by the company, the suffix letter S (for *surélevé* or raised) signifying that the engine was mounted with a slight downward angle in order to increase its thrust properties. In Russia, at the Anatra factory in Odessa, the Voisin Type LA.S was taken as the basis of a locally-built version of the French bomber, with modifications designed by Lientenant V. Ivanov of the Imperial Russian Air Service. Known as the VI (Voisin Ivanov), it was powered by a 150hp Salmson (Canton-Unné) engine and up to 150 were produced between March 1915 and March 1916. Due to extremely poor stability and a lack of adequate lateral control, many of these were lost in crashes and the whole Russian programme was a dismal failure. Ivanov tested a modified version in early 1917 which was somewhat better, but the crashes continued and the Voisin Ivanov was finally categorised as quite unfit for fighting purposes.

The next military version, the Voisin 4, was similarly available in standard and *surélevé* versions (Types LB and LB.S). It differed from the Voisin 3 chiefly in having

Henry Farré's painting shows a formation of Voisin bombers assembling for a daylight raid. Voisin bombers retained the same basic layout throughout World War I

Voisin 5 (Type LA.S)

Dimensions
Wingspan 14·75 m (48 ft 5 in)
Length 9·53 m (31 ft 3 in)

Engine
One 150 hp Salmson
(Canton-Unné)

Performance
Maximum speed 105 km/h (65 mph)
Ceiling 3,500 m (11,500 ft)

Armament
One 8 mm Hotchkiss machine gun
or one 37 mm cannon
60 kg (130 lb) of bombs

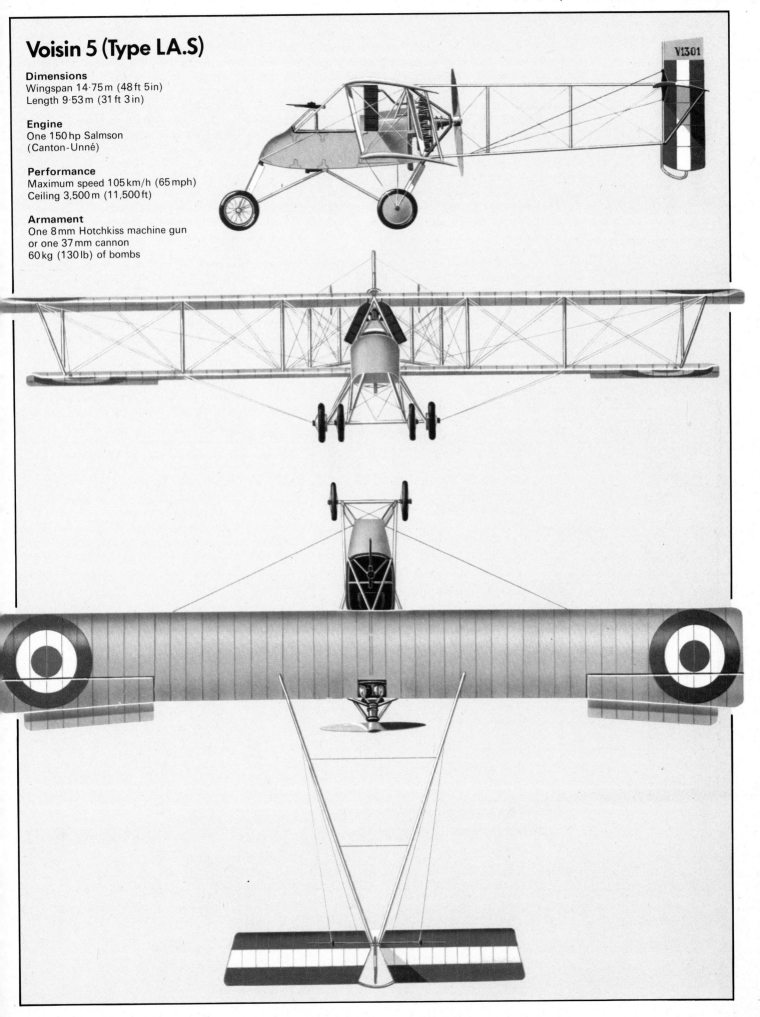

slightly staggered mainplanes, a more rectangular crew nacelle, and (in the LB.S) a 47mm Hotchkiss cannon mounted in the nose. This 'gunbus' was used primarily for ground strafing, and also, on occasion, as an escort. The first LB was flown in March 1915 and the LB.S towards the end of the same year. About 200 were built, and some of these, as well as some Voisin 3s, were converted for use as dual-control trainers. The Voisin 5 of late 1915, also known as Type LA.S, differed from the 3 LA.S in having a 150hp Salmson radial, a larger trailing-edge cut-out in the upper wing and a reinforced landing gear. Production, which totalled 350, was followed by that of the Voisin 6, which was virtually identical except in having a modified version of the Salmson engine rated at 155hp.

The last chicken coop

By way of the Voisin 7 reconnaissance aircraft, the company evolved the second most numerous model, the enlarged and structurally stronger Voisin 8. It was produced initially in Type LA.P form as a night bomber and entered service in this capacity in late 1916. By this time the Voisins' performance had been overtaken by that of more modern designs, and these were the first two of a

series of versions in which an attempt was made to achieve a worthwhile increase in performance in the later years of the war. Power plant in the Voisin 8 was a 220hp Peugeot and the two streamlined fuel tanks mounted on the struts beneath the upper mainplane were a distinctive recognition feature of this and later Voisin types. The LA.P version of the Voisin 8 was normally armed with one or two machine-guns and could carry a bomb-load of up to 180kg (400lb). The corresponding 'gunbus' version was the Type LB.P, with a 37mm or 47mm Hotchkiss cannon mounted in the front cockpit, but relatively few of the 1,123 Voisin 8s built were of this model. All went to the French Aviation Militaire–which was down to a mere 51 examples of the type by August 1918–except for 20 supplied to the Marine Nationale and nine bought by the United States Government and used for training. A lighter version of the Type LA.P received the military designation Voisin 9, but only a few of these were built.

The Voisin 10, 900 of which were produced, was delivered to the Aviation Militaire from early 1918 and was intended as a replacement for the Voisin 8, whose Peugeot engine had proved less than satisfactory. In its place, the Voisin 10 was powered by a 300hp Renault, which was not only more reliable but was also able to sustain more effectively the Voisin 10's performance at altitude. The extra power also meant that the bomb-load could be increased to about 300kg (660lb), with some sacrifice in range. Again, both bomber (Type LA.R) and gunbus (Type LB.R) models were produced, but the latter version, armed with a 37mm Hotchkiss, appeared in fairly small numbers only. Two Voisin 10s were purchased in July 1918 by the American Expeditionary Force. The final 'chicken coop' was the Voisin 11; 20 of these were built following its appearance in the summer of 1918.

Once again, as in 1908–10, Voisin's policy seems to have been to find a safe formula and stick to it, regardless of the pace with which aviation was developing all around him. With the ending of World War I he quit aviation altogether, redirecting his efforts instead into the automobile industry. He died on Christmas Day, 1973.

Left: the 'gunbus' version of the Voisin 10 of 1918 mounted a 37mm Hotchkiss cannon in the front of the nacelle.
Below: a flying ambulance version of the Voisin bomber was developed for service with the Aviation Militaire

Richthofen's Rival

World War I ace Werner Voss was considered by many to be the Red Baron's equal in air combat

Werner Voss was born at Krefeld near Düsseldorf on 13 April 1897. Had war not come, he would doubtless have entered his father's business of cloth processing, but instead he enlisted in the 2nd Westphalian Hussar Regiment No 11 and served with it in Russia. During his service there he was promoted to *unteroffizier* and awarded the Iron Cross, Second Class. He transferred to the Air Service on 1 August 1915 and, following training, served as a *vizefeldwebel* pilot flying two-seater machines of Kampfstaffel 20 in Kampfgeschwader IV on fighting and bombing operations during the Battle of Verdun.

Following promotion to commissioned officer rank, Leutnant Voss began to make a name for himself as a fighter pilot flying Albatross DII single-seaters. He arrived at Jagdstaffel 2 on 25 November 1916 and two days later was able to shoot down two enemy aircraft, a Nieuport at Miraumont in the morning and an FE2b pusher south of Bapaume in the early afternoon. These marked the beginning of a series of double victories.

January 1917 was a fairly uneventful time for Voss's unit, which now proudly bore the name of Jagdstaffel Boelcke in honour of its famous founder leader. Voss, who in the meantime had been decorated with the Iron Cross, First Class, did not have any successes, but in February he was able to score eight victories, half of them being of the 'two in one day' variety. He brought down a de Havilland DH2 on 1 February at Essarts, a BE2d at Givenchy on the 4th and another DH2 south-west of Serre on the 10th. Victories over two DH2 machines at St Catherine and Le Sauveur on the 25th comprised the first double of the month. The second double comprised two BEs at Blaineville and St Catherine on the 27th, separated by a single victory the previous day.

Voss had been lucky to survive his initial combats, but fighting in the air held no fears for him and he pressed home his attacks with a determination which few other pilots possessed. He had complete disregard for his personal safety and the fighting spirit and dash that he displayed in his early combats never left him. This necessary ingredient for a successful air fighter was enhanced by his ever-improving flying skills. In addition, Voss took a very keen interest in his aeroplane, its engine, guns and ammunition, and when he was not flying he was to be found in the hangar working with his mechanics.

March 1917 saw his victory score mounting steadily; an RE8 shot down south of Berneville on the 4th was followed by a DH2 at Favreuil on the 6th and another double was achieved on 11 March when an FE2b at Combles and a Nieuport south-west of Bailleul fell to his guns. Six days later an FE2b and a DH2 brought down north of Warlencourt afforded yet another double victory as did two BE2d machines at Neuville and Boyelles respectively on 18 March.

It was common practice for pilots to obtain a souvenir from the machines that they shot down, and the combat report that Voss rendered after bringing down the BE2d at Boyelles on 18 March tells how he landed alongside the the crashed machine and removed its two machine guns,

which were later handed over to Infantry Regiment No 107. He then set the wreckage on fire before taking-off again just before the arrival of enemy cavalry. Officially credited with 22 victories, Voss was awarded the Knight's Cross of the Royal House Order of Hohenzollern with Swords and found himself as the leading pilot in Jagdstaffel Boelcke. While some of the credit for his success was due to the fine performance of the Albatros DIII, which at this time was superior to the enemy machines, his dedication to the job and his ability to extract maximum benefit from the experience which he was accumulating

Werner Voss (above) was one of the first German front-line pilots to be allotted a Fokker DrI Triplane. He is pictured (below) with his aircraft on Courtrai aerodrome in September 1917, the month in which he fell in combat with SE5A scouts of No 56 Squadron, RFC

Below: Voss received his Fokker DrI Triplane in August 1917 and quickly took advantage of its superior handling qualities to register a number of combat victories. Due to power plant difficulties, early Triplanes utilised captured Le Rhônes

allowed him to develop into a skilled air fighter.

Voss had known Manfred von Richthofen since the days when they, had arrived together in Jagdstaffel 2 and there was a friendly rivalry between them. At the beginning of April with their victory scores at 23 and 31 respectively, Richthofen's 'greatest rival' was, by his own admission, Voss. There was, however, a marked difference in temperament between the two – the eager, headstrong Voss who would take on any enemy at any time, and the cool calculating Richthofen.

Voss only scored two victories in April, since he went home on leave after being awarded Germany's highest military decoration, the Pour le Mérite on 8 April. As a result he missed the air battles of 'Bloody April', during which the Germans enjoyed aerial superiority over northern France. However, he was able to gain five victories after his return from leave in the less hectic pace of aerial operations then taking place, before he was posted to Jagdstaffel 5 as acting Staffelführer on 20 May. He scored another six victories with this unit before he was moved again a month later, firstly to Jagdstaffel 29 then on to Jagdstaffel 14 as acting Staffelführer. He only obtained one victory with the latter unit before being posted as Staffelführer to Jagdstaffel 10, a component unit of Richthofen's Jagdgeschwader I.

This had been a period of continual change for Voss, who in a period of ten weeks had not only served with three different *jagdstaffeln*, but had undertaken some official visits to Germany. During one of these he had flown the prototype of a new triplane fighter built by the Fokker works at Schwerin. This machine, powered by a 110 hp rotary engine, could climb to 5,000 m (16,500 ft) in 18 minutes and was highly-manoeuvrable. It was a machine which pleased Voss, but although 20 were ordered in July, delivery was held up by the shortage of suitable engines. Two pre-production examples were ready by mid-August, powered with captured Le Rhône engines, and these were sent to the front on 21 August, Voss receiving one.

At the beginning of September, Richthofen had two successful combats while flying the other Fokker Triplane and was most enthusiastic about the new machine. Voss

Above: it was standard practice for pilots to remove parts from their victims' aircraft as prizes. Voss (right) is pictured with the engine from a kill.
Right: Voss was frequently compared with his famous compatriot, Manfred von Richthofen (right), with whom he is seen.
Far right: then Staffelführer of Jagdstaffel 18, Voss (right) accompanies the Austro-Hungarian Crown Prince on a tour of inspection

Below: pictured prior to a sortie over the Front, Werner Voss flew the Albatros DIII with Jagdstaffel Boelcke in early 1917. His personal aircraft bore several insignia on the fuselage, which are clearly visible here. Voss was posted to Jagdstaffel 5 in May 1917

took to the triplane naturally and found its extreme manoeuvrability a great change from the handling qualities of the Pfalz D III and Albatros DV, and he began to reduce the gap between his own victory score and Richthofen's total, the latter having gone home on leave. Voss brought down a Sopwith Camel on 3 September, scored a double two days later, and an FE2d on 6 September brought his victory score to 42. Four days later he was credited with three victories and the following day he scored a double. On 15 September Jagdgeschwader I's other Triplane was shot

down while being flown by Oberleutnent Kurt Wolff, Staffelführer of Jagdstaffel 11.

On the morning of 23 September Voss brought down a DH4 in flames, which is recorded as his 48th victory. In the evening there was considerable aerial activity on both sides of the Front, mostly below the main cloud base at 2,700m (9,000ft). These conditions were particularly suited to Voss and his Triplane, as they resulted in plenty of targets at the lower altitudes where the Fokker Triplane performed at its best. Voss soon attacked an SE5A of No 60 Squadron which was hit several times by his fire. As he followed the smoking machine, another SE5A came to its assistance; the Triplane turned on it in a flash and after a few shots this machine too had to retire.

Single-handed battle

While these initial combats were taking place, however, a formation of SE5A machines from No 56 Squadron led by Captain J. T. B. McCudden was diving on Voss. When he saw the British flyers approaching at high speed, Voss turned to meet them and fired at one of their number to such effect that it spun away and retired. Another formation of SE5A fighters from No 56 Squadron led by Captain G. H. Bowman now came to the assistance of McCudden's flight. The triplane was then surrounded by the British single-seaters, flown by some of the finest pilots in the Royal Flying Corps. Voss turned on each of his adversaries, firing at them and hitting them all in turn. Anyone getting behind him could not keep the triplane in their sights for any length of time. As soon as they opened fire, the triplane would flick round very quickly in a flat skidding turn and fire at its attacker. Another British machine, hit in the radiator and leaving a trail of water vapour was forced to leave the battle which had now dropped to 600m (2,000ft). The agile rotary-engined triplane was frequently able to zoom above the fight, which was now almost over the front line. Voss could have got away to the east, had he chosen, but he stayed and continued to dive into the turning British fighters.

Eventually, after Second Lieutenant A. P. F. Rhys Davids had fired at the triplane which was flying straight for the first time during the whole fight, its movements became very erratic. It turned towards the British lines, entered a steep dive and hit the ground at Plum Farm just north of Frezenberg. Such a flat turn as Voss had been using could only have been achieved by applying full rudder and opposite aileron, a fine method of turning through 180 degrees, producing at the same time a skidding target which was hard to hit. However, frequent use of the controls in this way could have led to their overstressing. It is possible that Voss, after 10 minutes of violent dog-fighting, lost the use of his rudder and, forced to fly straight, was unable to evade Rhys Davids' fire.

Some German sources have given Voss credit for destroying 50 enemy aeroplanes before he fell in action. Considering the frequent moves that he experienced over three months before his posting to Jagdgeschwader I, his was a fine performance and Voss was rated by many Royal Flying Corps and German pilots as a greater air fighter than Richthofen himself.

There was little elation amongst the British pilots at the death of Voss—many would have liked to see him brought down alive. Indeed it was a British pilot, McCudden, who wrote his epitaph which appeared in the *Daily Mail* on 14 June 1918: '. . . as long as I live I shall never forget my admiration for that German pilot, who single-handed fought seven of us for ten minutes, and also put some bullets through all of our machines.'

CHANCE VOUGHT'S CORSAIRS

American aircraft designer Chance Milton Vought had an almost singular devotion to improvement. Although his aviation career lasted less than two decades, Vought established a precedent of challenging existing principles which his successors have followed ever since. Born in New York City on 26 February 1890, Vought was taught the value of craftsmanship and wise money management by his father, an immigrant boat builder.

Reconfigured Wright design

In 1910, Vought began pilot training under the direction of Max Lillie, who ran a small flying school in Cicero, Illinois. The following year Vought qualified for Federation Aéronautique International licence No 156. After refining his flying skills further, Vought became consulting engineer of the Aero Club of Illinois in 1912 and, a year later, he joined his mentor at the Lillie Aviation School. While serving as aeronautical engineer and instructor at the school, the 23-year-old pilot modified a conventional Wright pusher biplane. Vought reconfigured the Wright design as a tractor type with larger propellers which improved the aircraft's performance. The Vought-Wright Tractor biplane provoked the criticism of some of Vought's

Left: the most famous Vought aircraft was the F4U Corsair fighter of World War II, which gave distinguished service with the United States Navy and Marine Corps, the Fleet Air Arm, and the Royal New Zealand Air Force in the Pacific.
Below left: the LTV A-7 Corsair II is in fact the third Vought aircraft to be named Corsair. An A-7E of VA-192 serving aboard USS Kitty Hawk (CVA-63) is pictured.
Above: the VE-7 and the VE-9 (illustrated) were advanced trainers intended for the US Army.
Below: the VE-7 was produced for the US Navy after World War I and served in training and operational roles

contemporaries, who were upset that he had the temerity to alter the design which launched the era of powered flight. However, Vought felt he was vindicated by the aircraft's improved performance.

In 1914, Chance Vought became editor of the pioneer American aviation weekly publication *Aero and Hydro*. In the same year he also joined the Mayo Brothers Radiator Works in New Haven, Connecticut, where he designed an advanced training aircraft prototype subsequently purchased by the British Government.

In 1916, Vought worked successively for the Wright Company in Dayton, Ohio and the Wright-Martin Company in Cleveland, Ohio. As World War I grew in ferocity, however, Chance Vought recognised there would be a great need for military aircraft and he formed a production company with his father-in-law, Birdseye B. Lewis. Early in 1917 the Lewis & Vought Company opened for business on the third floor of a small factory building in Long Island City, New York.

For the new firm's first venture Vought designed a two-seat biplane training aircraft that would withstand the rigours of inexperienced student pilots and be uncomplicated enough to be serviced by mechanics new to the trade. This was the VE-7, powered by the 150hp Hispano-Suiza Model A engine then being produced by Vought's former employer, the Wright-Martin Company. In appearance the VE-7 looked like a de Havilland DH4 with the cowling of a SPAD, but the similarity ended there. The VE-7 was faster than virtually all contemporary trainers and often replaced the Curtiss JN-4, Standard M and Avro 504 in the US training programme.

Unusual testing facilities
The first Lewis & Vought Company aircraft were produced in absurdly cramped facilities. Aircraft were first built in the third floor factory area, then dismantled and lowered out of a window in sections by pulley and reassembled on the ground. Engine tests were conducted in an equally unique atmosphere. Lacking a formal airport, Lewis & Vought Company production crews would lash the tail of a new aircraft to a telegraph pole in front of the factory; with take-off along the narrow street thus averted, engine testing was begun.

When the underpowered Curtiss JN-4D was fitted with the Hispano-Suiza engine, thereby becoming the JN-4H, performance was improved to the extent that fewer VE-7 aircraft were needed. Hence, only 14 VE-7s were actually delivered to the US Army. At one point late in the war the Army ordered two VE-7s with the improved 180hp Wright-Hispano E engine. Although this variant

did not go into production for the Army, it did attract interest among aviation planners in the US Navy and became the first of a long line of Vought aircraft produced specifically for the Navy.

To augment the Lewis & Vought Company's production facilities, the US Navy also produced VE-7s at its Naval Aircraft Factory in Philadelphia, Pennsylvania. Initially, the Navy ordered 20 training variants in October 1919. These were so superior to the Aeromarine 39 and Curtiss N-9 types then in service, that the order was expanded to 128 – a healthy production run at the time. The first aircraft were standard VE-7 two-seat trainers. In March 1920, however, the first VE-7G aircraft arrived; later designated VE-9 aircraft, these machines were armed with a forward-firing synchronised Vickers machine gun and a 0·3 in Lewis machine gun in the rear cockpit.

American naval aviation was less than a decade old when the first Lewis & Vought Company aircraft began to arrive. They came at a time of rapid expansion and when it became evident that the VE-7/VE-9 series was far more than a two-seat training aircraft, the type was quickly adapted to other duties. One variant, the VE-7S, was produced as a single-seat fighter and armed first with a synchronised Vickers machine gun and, later, a Browning gun. Since the pilot sat in the rear cockpit of the VE-7 series aircraft, the vacant front seat of the fighter variant was used to hold the ammunition feeding and shell ejection equipment for the machine gun.

First carrier operations

The VE-9H floatplane variant added to the over-water versatility of the series, but it was the VE-7SF – a landplane equipped with flotation gear for emergency landings in the water – which made the first take-off from the US Navy's first aircraft carrier. Much impressed by early aircraft carrier operations conducted by the Royal Navy, the US Navy converted the collier USS *Jupiter* into an aircraft carrier by adding a flight deck above the ship's superstructure. Renamed USS *Langley* (CV-1) in honour of American aviation pioneer Samuel Pierpont Langley, the ship was commissioned on 20 March 1922.

Early carrier operations in the VE-7/VE-9 series aboard USS *Langley* were part of a precarious learning process undertaken by fledgling naval aviators. One of those early carrier pilots, the late Rear Admiral Jackson Tate, described a take-off in this way: 'A trough about six feet long, set up on sawhorses, was rigged on the aft end of the flight deck. When the Vought's tail skid was placed in the trough she was in the flight attitude. We had no brakes, so the plane was held down on the deck by a wire with a bomb release at the end. This was attached to a ring on the landing gear. The pilot then climbed in, turned up the old Hispano engine to full revs, and gave the "go" signal. The bomb release was snapped, the Vought leaped forward and was airborne almost immediately.'

Chance Vought's father-in-law and business partner Birdseye B. Lewis retired from the firm in 1922. The company was then reorganised as the Chance Vought Corporation, in which the new president also served as chief designer and test supervisor. The following year a much-improved variant of the VE-7/9 series was delivered to the US Navy. The new two-seat observation biplane was designated UO-1 under a new Navy identification system using the first letter for the manufacturer – in this case U for Vought since V denoted heavier-than-air craft as a class – the second letter for the type (observation) and the numeral to indicate that this was the first of the class to be built by Vought for the Navy under the new system.

Above: the cruiser USS Richmond carried two Vought UO-1 catapult-launched scout aircraft. Left: the single-seat float fighter version of the UO-1, the FU-1, mounted twin machine guns over the faired-over front cockpit. Right: first of the Corsairs, the Vought O2U-1 first prototype is pictured in 1927. Below right: the XSBU-1 was the first Vought aircraft fitted with an enclosed cockpit and the last of the company's biplane designs to be built for the US Navy

The UO-1 airframe was nearly identical to that of the VE series but, in keeping with Chance Vought's penchant for improvement, the new aircraft was considerably more streamlined, particularly in the vertical tail surfaces. The UO-1 was powered by a 220 hp Wright J-1 radial engine which gave the aircraft a top speed of 200 km/h (124 mph) at sea level, an improvement over the VE's performance.

Catapult-launched floatplane

Float-equipped UO-1 aircraft gradually replaced the VE types assigned as catapult-launched observation aircraft to operate from capital ships, as well as from other vessels whose aircraft took off from and landed on the water. Much later in the life of the series, on 3 July 1929, Lieutenant A. W. Gorton's UO-1 made the US Navy's first hook-on landing beneath the airship *Los Angeles*.

A single-seat fighter variant, designated the FU-1 under the 1923 system, was developed to meet Navy requirements for a catapult-launched floatplane fighter assigned to battleships. Introduced in 1925 and powered by a 200 hp Wright J-3 air-cooled radial engine, Vought's FU-1 was the US military's last 'all wood and wire' aircraft. They were all assigned to fighter squadron VF-2B, which dispersed them amongst the 12 battleships in the US Navy, and served until 1928. At that point, the remaining FU-1s were converted to two-seat FU-2 aircraft and relegated to utility and training missions.

Chance Vought's successor to the UO series proved to be more than just another reliable aircraft from a manu-

facturer of proven ability. It was also a radical, but practical, departure in structure, having an all tubular steel fuselage. Moreover, the new observation biplane was the first Navy aircraft designed specifically for the new 450hp Pratt & Whitney R-1340-88 engine – better known as the Wasp.

Two prototypes were ordered in 1926. Since the US Navy had not yet adopted the 'X' designation for experimental aircraft, the two biplane observation craft were designated O2U-1, being the first variant of the second observation aircraft built by Vought for the Navy. As in the UO series, the two O2U crewmen sat in tandem open cockpits. The pilot's armament consisted of one fixed forward-firing 0·3in machine gun mounted in the top wing. The observer could, if needed, be provided with a pair of flexible 0·3in machine guns on a Scarff ring.

Fully-loaded and with armament in place, the aircraft displayed performance characteristics nearly equal to those of lighter, single-seat fighters. The prototype reportedly reached its 5,500m (18,000ft) service ceiling in ten minutes. While not expecting a slow, lumbering observation aircraft, naval authorities did not anticipate that the O2U-1 would be quite so agile. Upon its return to the Anacostia Naval Air Station, outside Washington DC, the prototype was fitted with pontoon floats and tested in the seaplane configuration.

All-metal framework

The new Corsair retained some distinctly individual characteristics of previous Vought designs, including the 'cheek mounted' fuel tank and fuselage streamlining. These were complemented by novel features developed during further testing of the Corsair series. The all-metal framework, for example, proved better able to absorb the shock of being launched from the Mark 1 compressed-air catapult then in use aboard US Navy ships. Yet, this stability was not achieved at the expense of added weight, thus allowing the Corsair to fulfill its role as a high-speed reconnaissance aircraft.

During the month of April 1927, three world records were set by the prototype O2U-1, which had a distinctive appearance with its non-standard propeller spinner. Flown in the floatplane configuration, the O2U-1 had to conform to Class C seaplane specifications, which included hauling a useful load of 500 kg (1,100 lb). Hence, some of the military 'load'—including the observer—was removed and replaced by 500 kg of dead weight. On 14 April, Lieutenant G. R. Henderson took off from Anacostia and attained the record altitude of 6,760 m (22,178 ft). The prototype was then flown to Hampton Roads, Virginia, where on 23 April Lieutenant S. W. Calloway flew it to set a new 100 km world speed record of 237 km/h (147 mph). Calloway's achievement is of particular interest since 227 km/h (141 mph) was the best average speed reached the year before by unloaded observation landplanes at the National Air Races in Philadelphia. Finally, on 30 April, Lieutenant J. D. Barner went over the same triangular course at Hampton Roads and broke the 500 km speed record by clocking 219 km/h (136 mph). O2U-1 aircraft were assigned to US Navy and Marine Corps squadrons during the remainder of 1927 and into 1928. The Corsair became standard equipment with the battleship-based observation squadrons VO-3B, VO-4B and VO-5B, as well as with scouting squadron VS-1B aboard USS *Langley*.

Rough-field operations

The O2U-1 made history in January 1928, when First Lieutenant 'Frank' Schilt, a member of Marine Corps observation squadron VO-7M, made a series of hazardous flights in support of ground operations in Nicaragua. The US Marines were in the Central American nation to quell local insurgents when their outpost in the town of Quilali was surrounded by overwhelming enemy forces. The Marine squadron commander, Major R. E. Rowell, suggested sending an aircraft to bring badly-needed supplies to the town. Thus, while men of the Quilali garrison prepared a landing strip, VO-7M maintenance personnel fitted an O2U-1 with the undercarriage from an old de Havilland DH4 to enable the Corsair to make a landing on the rough ground.

Lieutenant Schilt volunteered for the mission and made his first flight over the town on 6 January. Once past the insurgents' territory, Schilt had an area 30 m (100 ft) wide and 150 m (500 ft) long from which to operate. During the next three days he made ten flights into Quilali. Each time men had to run out and grab the wingtips of the O2U Corsair to keep it from running off the short landing strip. In the unmanned observer's cockpit, Lieutenant Schilt carried medical supplies and provisions on the way in and wounded personnel on the trip out.

The modified landing gear took the stress of the rugged terrain, but during Schilt's eighth landing the tail-skid collapsed. The centre-section struts were badly bent in the next landing, but Schilt still had one more trip to make. As in previous flights, Schilt's last hop out of Quilali was punctuated by enemy ground fire. Lieutenant Schilt's heroism in an O2U-1 was recognised with the awarding of the Medal of Honour.

By August of 1928, new Corsairs had replaced all 34 UO-1s in three of the Battleship Divisions and made their appearance aboard five of the six ships in two of the Light Cruiser Divisions. Cruisers of the Asiatic Fleet also began operating the O2U at this time. Since the three Loening OL-6 and three OL-8 amphibian aircraft aboard the four remaining battleships were more versatile than the Corsairs, Vought developed an amphibious float for the

O2U-1 in 1928. That year also saw production of the next variant, the O2U-2, which had a larger rudder, dihedral on the lower wing and a somewhat different cut-out shape in the centre-section of the top wing.

As the series progressed, further production of the Corsair was ordered by the US Navy and, in one instance, the US Army. A total of 80 O2U-3s was delivered to the Navy and one of the same type, designated O-28, to the Army for testing. These aircraft differed slightly from the preceding variant and, in turn, differed little from the 42 O2U-4s subsequently ordered.

Overseas interest in the Corsair became evident in 1929, when the Mitsui Trading Company of Japan purchased a single O2U-1 from Vought. In keeping with the custom of the time, a complete set of blueprints was included in the purchase price of the aircraft. From these plans 150 oriental variants were produced by Nakajima as carrier-based reconnaissance aircraft and designated Type 90, Model 3. A slight alteration of the rudder design distinguished the Japanese copy.

The American company, however, was too busy with corporate and production matters to challenge design piracy. During that same year, Chance Vought's company became a division of the United Aircraft and Transportation Company (later United Aircraft Corporation). Among the projects being developed was a two-seat catapult-launched fighter variant of the O2U. Designated XF2U-1, one example was built and tested, but did not lead to a production contract.

New production facility

As part of the Vought company's incorporation into the United Aircraft complex, production facilities were moved in 1930 from Long Island City, New York to East Hartford, Connecticut, where a modern, spacious plant was being built. Although in failing health, Chance Vought actively participated in planning the new facility. Then, stricken with septicaemia, he returned to his Southampton, Long Island home and died in a nearby hospital on 26 July 1930. He was 40 years old.

Vought's work was carried on, however, in such projects as the amphibious float designs for existing Corsair aircraft. The Vought floats were produced by the fledgling Grumman Aircraft Engineering Corporation, which subsequently became a major supplier of US Navy aircraft. The Grumman float was later fitted to the next generation of the Corsair series, the O3U-1, which evolved from the O2U-4.

A much smoother design and fitted with a cowled 450 hp Pratt & Whitney R-1340C Wasp engine, the O3U-1 of 1931 became the first major type produced by Vought in its new Connecticut facility. Aside from the greater use of the Grumman amphibious float on the O3U-1, major changes did not occur until the O3U-2, which was so different that all 29 aircraft in the series were redesignated in the Fleet purely for scouting purposes as the SU-1. The aircraft was powered by a 600 hp Pratt & Whitney R-1690C Hornet engine in a low drag cowling. This and other design changes—such as a small dorsal fin on the rear fuselage top deck and a different rudder design—contributed to an increase in the maximum speed by nearly 64 km/h (40 mph) to 274 km/h (170 mph).

Still considered part of the Corsair series, the SU-1 entered Fleet service in 1932. Among the first units to receive the new aircraft were the only two US Marine Corps scouting squadrons deployed aboard aircraft carriers before World War II, these being VS-14M aboard USS *Saratoga* (CV-3) and VS-15M aboard USS *Lexington*

Right: the Vought OS2U Kingfisher was the US Navy's most successful shipboard scouting aeroplane of World War II, over 1,000 being built. A Kingfisher is pictured aboard the battleship USS Arkansas in 1944. Below: a Kingfisher spots for naval gunfire during the assault of Anguar Island on 17 September 1944

(CV-2). Navy squadrons aboard both carriers, as well as units assigned to USS *Langley*—which was considered more of an experimental than an operational aircraft carrier, despite its long service life—also received complements of SU aircraft. The three fighter squadrons—VF-1B, VF-2S and VF-3B—aboard each of the carriers were each also assigned one SU in addition to their Boeing fighters.

While the O3U and SU Corsairs underwent further development, Vought's export business expanded on the basis of earlier variants. In 1932, the Brazilian air force bought 15 Vought V-65-B observation aircraft, which were based on the successful SU-1 design. The next year, an order for a cowled version of the O2U-3 was placed by the Dominican Republic. At least one example of a similar aircraft fitted with streamlined wheel fairings and designated Vought V-66-E was purchased by the Royal Air Force and, bearing the RAF serial number K3561, was evaluated at Martlesham Heath, Suffolk.

In 1934, the Vought V-80-P, similar in appearance to the O3U-3, was displayed in RAF livery, but it was never actually acquired by the Air Ministry. From that proposed export variant came the V-80, a single-seat fighter with an enclosed cockpit and four fixed machine guns. Intended to offer long range, the V-80 was fitted with a 654 litre (173 US gallons) fuel tank. The V-80's 700 hp Pratt & Whitney TIC-1 Hornet engine gave the aircraft a top speed reported as 'comparing favourably with the finest single-seat fighters in service', but the next production fighter from Vought was still some years away.

First scout-bomber

It was in pursuit of a successful two-seat fighter design, however, that Vought evolved its next production aircraft. On 30 June 1932, Vought was awarded a Navy contract to produce a prototype designated XF3U-1. The following

May the company unveiled a biplane of conventional metal and fabric construction powered by a fully-cowled 625 hp Pratt & Whitney R-1535-64 two-row radial engine. Six months later the Navy had Vought modify the experimental fighter design into a scout-bomber. Designated XSBU-1, Vought's first scout-bomber for the Navy had a larger internal fuel capacity, larger and stronger wings and a greater external load capability than intended for the proposed fighter. The Navy placed a production order for 84 SBU-1 aircraft in January 1935, with deliveries to begin in November. The SBU was to be Vought's last biplane design for the Navy.

Dimensions
Span 12·49 m (41 ft)
Length 11·06 m (33 ft 4 in)

Engine
One 2,000 hp Pratt & Whitney R-2800-8W
Twin Wasp

Performance
Maximum speed 671 km/h (417 mph) at
6,000 m (19,900 ft)
Range 1,633 km (1,015 miles)
Service ceiling 12,800 m (36,900 ft)

Armament
Six 0·5 in Browning machine guns
Up to 450 kg (1,000 lb) of bombs

Vought F4U-1A Corsair of VMF-111, US Marine Corps

*Above: because of early
problems in operating
from carriers, the first
US Navy Corsairs went
into action from island
airstrips in the Pacific.
Right: the Corsair's
distinctive inverted
gull wing is shown to
advantage in this view
of an F4U-1.
Top far right: the
experimental V-173
Flying Pancake of 1942
had remarkable low-speed
flying characteristics.
Above far right: the F7U
Cutlass was one of the
first US Navy fighters
to be armed with
air-to-air missiles*

A further 40 aircraft designated SBU-2 were ordered and subsequently assigned to US Naval Reserve squadrons. Meanwhile, the Vought Corporation, which had been merged with Russian-born Igor Sikorsky's company to form the Vought-Sikorsky Division of United Aircraft Corporation, was already at work on a successor. The SB2U-1 was an all-metal low-wing monoplane with the two-man crew seated in tandem beneath a 'greenhouse' canopy. Called the Vought Vindicator, it was the firm's first design to employ retractable landing gear. In addition to the 42 examples produced for the Navy, 50 SB2U-1s were delivered to Britain under the export designation V-156-BI Chesapeake Mark I, while 40 of the same type, designated V-156-F, were acquired by France in 1939. Export models had the 750 hp Pratt & Whitney Twin Wasp Junior engine.

SB2U-1 and SB2U-2 Vindicators were subsequently assigned to several aircraft carrier air groups, while the SB2U-3 variant was issued almost entirely to US Marine Corps squadrons. During the Battle of Midway on 5 June 1942, SB2Us from Marine scout-bombing squadron VMSB-241 attacked one of the Japanese strike forces heading for Midway. In the course of that encounter, Captain R. E. Fleming's SB2U was hit and began to smoke heavily; Fleming turned the stricken aircraft and crashed it into the Japanese battleship IJNS *Mikuma*, for which action he was posthumously awarded the Medal of Honour.

Wartime production
Following the attack on 7 December 1941 by Japanese naval forces on American installations at Pearl Harbour, Hawaii, the United States entered the Pacific War in full

force. In addition to the SB2U series, which was soon phased out, the US Navy had two other Vought aircraft in its inventory. The first of these, the OS2U Kingfisher, was an observation and scouting aircraft which could be deployed either as a floatplane or with fixed landing gear. First delivered in August 1940, the type was in such demand later that Vought-Sikorsky production of the Kingfisher was augmented by the Naval Aircraft Factory, which built 300 versions of the OS2U-3 which were designated OS2N-1. Aircraft produced by both facilities saw extensive use throughout the war on patrol missions and in the search and rescue role in retrieving pilots forced to ditch in the water far from land.

Vought's other wartime standby was the company's fourth fighter produced for the Navy, the F4U series. Rex Beisel led the design team which created the unusual

inverted gull-wing, single-seat shipboard fighter. The F4U's distinctive design was required to accommodate the short, sturdy undercarriage needed for carrier operations while giving maximum height to one of the world's largest propellers. This latter was needed to handle the 2,000 hp 18-row Pratt & Whitney R-2800-8(W) Twin Wasp B engine, one of the most powerful engines ever installed in a piston-engined fighter. The unusual configuration also caused wind passing over wing-root air inlets to make a peculiar whistling sound which caused the Japanese to nickname the F4U 'whistling death'.

The F4U series was given the name 'Corsair', although it did not directly evolve from the earlier Corsair biplanes produced by Chance Vought; furthermore, the F4U Corsair did not adapt easily to carrier operations, unlike its illustrious predecessor. During the first carrier trials, aboard the escort carrier USS *Sangamon* (CVE-26) on 25 September 1942, test pilot Lieutenant Sam Porter noted a number of problems with the new fighter. Mainly handling problems that pilots had to learn to overcome in training, these were enough to keep the badly-needed carrier fighter away from shipboard operations for some time. However, the US Navy's initial loss was the Marine Corps' gain. On 7 September Marine fighter squadron VMF-124 became the first Corsair-equipped operational unit and was soon joined by other USMC squadrons which operated F4U Corsairs with great success.

St Valentine's Day Massacre
Despite the Corsair's great promise as a land-based fighter, it got off to a bad start. During VMF-124's second combat patrol, on 14 February 1943, the American aircraft group which the F4Us were accompanying was attacked by 50 Japanese Mitsubishi Zero-sen fighters. Two of the Corsairs, two Consolidated Liberator bombers, two Curtiss P-40 Warhawks and four Lockheed Lightnings fell to the guns of attackers during the fight, which has since become known as the 'St Valentine's Day Massacre'.

VMF-124 subsequently took its revenge by shooting down 68 Japanese aircraft, while suffering the loss of only four aircraft and three pilots. The squadron's most illustrious Corsair ace was a former enlisted pilot, First Lieutenant K. A. Walsh, who demonstrated just how tough the F4U was. During the Japanese attack on US shipping at Vella Lavella on 15 August 1943, Walsh broke through an enemy force six times greater than the American defenders; he shot down a fighter and two bombers. Over Kahili two weeks later, Walsh single-handedly attacked 50 Zeros and shot down four of them; his F4U was so badly damaged that he was forced to ditch just off the coast of Vella Lavella. These two encounters earned Walsh the Medal of Honour. He ended the war with 21 enemy aircraft to his credit, all scored while flying Corsairs.

During the battle of Rabaul on the island of New Britain, from 1 October 1943 to 17 February 1944, US Marine Corps F4Us accounted for an unusually high number of Japanese aircraft destroyed. In aerial combat, 330 Zeros were brought down, while only 61 Corsairs were lost, while 160 Zeros were lost operationally, compared with 70 Corsairs. A total of 50 Zeros was destroyed on the ground, whereas no Corsairs were lost in this manner during this period.

In the hands of other Marine Corps pilots—most notably the 28-victory ace Colonel Gregory 'Pappy' Boyington, commander of VMF-214—Vought F4U aircraft were highly successful in a variety of combat roles. Improvements in the F4U training cycle led to the aircraft's successful use aboard aircraft carriers, beginning with Commander Tommy Blackburn's VF-17 unit during early strikes on Rabaul.

The Corsair also served as a night fighter. Equipped with airborne intercept (AI) radar in a special housing on the starboard wingtip, modified F4U-2 aircraft served with shore-based VF(N)-75 in New Guinea and aboard the carrier USS *Essex* (CV-9) with VF(N)-101. Other F4U-2s were deployed aboard USS *Hornet* (CV-10) and *Intrepid* (CV-11) and with VF(N)-532.

The Corsair design was in such demand that Vought-Sikorsky subcontracted production runs to other manufacturers, who under the Navy system applied some seemingly unusual designations to them. Hence, the 735 F3A aircraft were Corsairs built by the Brewster Aeronautical Corporation, while the Goodyear Tire & Rubber Company produced 4,014 Corsairs variously designated FG-1, -2 and -3. Goodyear modifications led to the FG-4 and the further refined F2G-1 and -2, none of which went into significant production.

Even the end of World War II did not herald the end of the Corsair line. In 1946, the XF4U-5 was introduced and led to production of 223 F4U-5s with the more powerful 2,300 hp Pratt & Whitney R-2800-32W engine and armed with four 20 mm wing guns. Following a move from Connecticut to Dallas, Texas in 1948, Vought also produced F4U-5N and -5NL night fighters and F4U-5P photo-reconnaissance variants.

The advent of jet-powered aircraft did not interrupt further refinement of the Corsair series. An F4U-6 variant conformed so well to the US Navy's requirements for a ground attack aircraft that it was redesignated AU-1 to denote it as the first Vought aircraft in that role. In all, 111 AU-1s were built and supplied to the US Marine

Top right and upper right: the RF-8 version of the Crusader was used for fast photo reconnaissance in the 1960s.
Above right and right: Corsair II attack aircraft replaced the Douglas Skyhawk aboard US Navy carriers from 1967

Corps, which used them during the Korean War in the early 1950s. The Navy subsequently ordered 94 F4U-7s, which were similar to the AU-1s, and supplied them to the French naval air arm for use in the Indo-China War. The Corsair assembly line was finally closed down in 1952.

Jet-powered Pirate

Chance Vought Corporation was one of a number of aircraft suppliers encouraged by the US Government during World War II to develop jet-powered aircraft. The Vought company responded with a short, bulbous-nosed aircraft designated XF6U and nicknamed the Pirate, to complement the image and the name of the highly suc-

cessful F4U series. However, the production F6U-1–powered by a 1,916kg (4,225lb) static thrust Westinghouse J34-WE-30 engine with afterburner–did not see wide service. Thirty production models were built and one was modified as an F6U-1P for photo-reconnaissance, but 35 additional machines on order were cancelled.

The conventional appearance of the F6U contrasted starkly with its unusual successor, the F7U Cutlass. Developed from German aeronautical research into tailless designs, the twin-engined aircraft had an unconventional control system. Elevons on the wings controlled pitch and roll, while directional control was effected by twin fins and rudders located at the ends of the centre-

LTV A-7D Corsair II
of the 354th TFW, US Air Force

Dimensions
Span 13·86m (38ft 9in)
Length 14·4m (46ft 1½in)

Engine
One 6,575kg (14,500lb) Allison TF41-A-1 turbofan

Performance
Maximum speed Mach 0·92 at 7,000m (23,000ft)
Tactical radius 1,120km (700 miles)

Armament
One 20mm M61 Vulcan cannon
Up to 6,800kg (15,000lb) of external stores

section. Modifications to the early F7U-1 and -2 designs led to the more successful F7U-3, of which 180 examples were ordered and assigned to VF-81, VF-83, VF-122 and VF-124. The Cutlass was one of the first Navy jet fighters to be equipped with guided missiles. When production ended in December 1955, 290 F7U-3 aircraft had been delivered.

In 1953, Vought began producing larger guided missiles with its successful Regulus I series. In the ensuing years the company built 514 of the type, which could be launched from submarines, aircraft carriers, cruisers, guided missile ships and converted landing ships. Equipped to carry nuclear warheads if the need arose, some of the jet-powered Regulus Is were built with wheels for flight tests and were landed by remote control from chase aircraft. Regulus II remained in service until replaced by the Polaris submarine-launched ballistic missile.

National speed record

In 1954, Chance Vought Aircraft became a separate company, splitting away from United Aircraft. The following year it won a Navy competition to produce a supersonic fighter to succeed the F7U Cutlass. Its design, the F8U Crusader, soon made an impressive mark by setting a new national speed record of 1,634 km/h (1,015 mph) in 1956. A year later Marine Corps Colonel John Glenn – who subsequently gained fame as the first American astronaut to orbit the earth – flew a Crusader across the United States at supersonic speeds to set a new transcontinental speed record for single-seat jet aircraft which remains unbroken in 1979. Glenn, now a United States Senator, flew an F8U-1P from Los Angeles, California to New York in three hours and 23 minutes. He averaged 1,164·39 km/h (723·52 mph), or Mach 1·1 at 10,670 m (35,000 ft).

By 1961, when Chance Vought Aircraft was merged with Ling-Temco, the F8U-3 was being replaced as the Fleet's top fighter by the new McDonnell F4H Phantom II. However, the Crusader proved to be as durable as many of its Vought predecessors. In 1964, the French navy took delivery of 42 F-8E aircraft and Vought contracted to rebuild and modernise 395 F-8 aircraft from 1966 to 1970. The type had been re-designated under the 1962 US armed forces integrated designation system.

During the Vietnam War, F-8s were used as fast photo-reconnaissance aircraft and as effective fighters. The US Navy's fifth MiG 'kill' of the war was scored by Commander H. L. Marr, commanding officer of VF-211, on 21 June 1966. Indeed, as part of the same fight, two other F-8s from VF-211 – piloted by Lieutenant E. J. Chaney and Lieutenant (junior grade) Phil Vampatella – returned to the aircraft carrier USS Hancock (CVA-19) each with a MiG-17 to its credit.

It is true that the F-8s were far superior to the MiG-17s. However, on subsequent occasions Crusader pilots took on the best of the North Vietnamese Air Force and won the day. On 1 August 1968, Lieutenant Norman McCoy in an F-8H from VF-51 aboard USS Bon Homme Richard (CVA-31) shot down a MiG-21 over North Vietnam. Less than two months later, on 19 September, Lieutenant Tony Nargi in a F-8C from VF-111 from USS Intrepid (CVS-11) shot down one MiG-21 and probably accounted for another, although this was not confirmed.

Tri-service transport

Vought entered a new field of aviation in 1964 by designing and building the most successful Vertical/Short Take-off and Landing (V/STOL) aircraft of its time, the XC-142 tri-service transport. Five of these aircraft were built and amassed 488 flights with 39 different military and civilian pilots at the controls. The programme was closed with the delivery of the last remaining experimental aircraft to the US Air Force Museum in 1969. The US National Aeronautics and Space Administration (NASA) had used the Vought V/STOL aircraft for a number of airport operations test flights following completion of the military experimental programme.

In 1964 Vought also began its next major production run when the company won a US Navy competition to produce a carrier-based attack aircraft to replace the Douglas A-4 Skyhawk. Ling-Temco-Vought (LTV), as the company became known, was successful in its bid to produce the A-7 largely because the new light attack aircraft was to be based on the F-8 Crusader design. The LTV A-7 which first flew on 27 September 1965 had a shorter fuselage than the F-8 and no afterburner. There was also less sweep-back to the wings, which did not have the varying wing incidence used by the F-8 to lower its landing speed.

LTV bestowed on the A-7 one of the company's most honoured names, dubbing the design the Corsair II. In point of fact, the A-7 was really the Corsair III, if its biplane predecessor is counted, but the new use of the name identified the turbofan-powered light attack aircraft as the successor to the famed F4U which served during World War II and the Korean War. Capable of a maximum speed of little more than half that of the Crusader, the A-7A entered US Navy service in the autumn of 1966 with deliveries of aircraft to two training squadrons, VA-122 and VA-174. On 1 February 1967, VA-147 was commissioned as the first front-line A-7A squadron and made its first carrier landings aboard USS Ranger (CVA-61) in the following June.

The US Air Force, which had earlier capitalised on a Navy-inspired combat design by ordering its own quantities of McDonnell F-4 aircraft, looked again at the Navy's inventory in 1966 and ordered a land-based variant, the A-7D. The USAF variant, however, was powered by the 6,365 kg (14,250 lb) static thrust Allison TF41-A-2, a licence-built Rolls-Royce Spey engine. The Navy, which had used the Pratt & Whitney TF30-P-6 turbofan in the A-7A and the 5,535 kg (12,200 lb) static thrust TF30-P-8 in the A-7B, switched to the Allison-built engine for the improved A-7E equipped with more sophisticated avionics and navigation equipment linked to a digital computer. Navy and Air Force A-7s flew more than 100,000 combat sorties in South-East Asia and dropped more than 200,000 tons of ordnance during some of the fiercest bombing and attack missions which marked the final phase of that conflict. Corsair IIs were used for close support, SAM missile site suppression, combat air patrol, interdiction, escort and aerial tanker operations.

The versatile A-7 continues in active squadron service, as well as with US Air National Guard and US Naval Air Reserve units. Moreover, the A-7H variant is used by the Hellenic air force of Greece, and a twin-engined version has been proposed to meet the US Navy's light-weight fighter (LWF) requirements. A number of earlier A-7B and A-7C aircraft has been converted into two-seat trainer aircraft designated TA-7C.

Now known as the Vought Corporation, a subsidiary of the LTV Corporation, the company is America's second oldest aircraft manufacturer in continuous production. Only the Boeing Airplane Company has been in business longer, having been founded a year before Birdseye Lewis and Chance Vought formed their company.

Warplanes from the West Coast

Born in 1900, Gerard (Jerry) Vultee was one of the leading designers of the infant Douglas company in the 1920s and with John Northrop was personally responsible for the switch to light-alloy primary structures. At Lockheed his *magnum opus* was the wooden Vega, followed by the record-breaking Sirius built for the Lindberghs. The brilliance of these designs resulted in a startling development. In 1932, at the height of the depression when many planemakers were starving, Vultee was handed a cheque for $50,000 and told 'Go build yourself a new company'.

His benefactor was tycoon E. L. Cord, whose empire included some of the top auto, engine and air-transport companies, and whose aircraft-building enterprises were in 1933 grouped into Aviation Corporation (Avco). Young Vultee took the cheque, left Lockheed, formed a company called Airplane Development Corporation and set to work with a growing team in a small hangar at the Grand Central Air Terminal at Glendale, California, then the main airport for Los Angeles. He had a clear directive from Cord: build a superior single-engined transport for Cord's American Airlines.

High-speed airliner

At that time such a task was assisted by the emergence of refined and reliable high-power engines and the new Hamilton variable-pitch propeller. Vultee chose the 675 hp Wright Cyclone and fitted it to one of the neatest and most streamlined aircraft ever built. Called the V-1, it was entirely of light-alloy stressed-skin construction. The absence of bracing struts was complete and the inward-retracting landing gears were especially attractive in an era when any retractable gear tended to be complicated and ungainly. As many as ten passengers – then

a figure typical of much larger machines – could be accommodated in great comfort, and a particular feature was the careful attention to interior soundproofing.

Vultee's team were renowned for fast work and, just a year after the company was formed, the V-1 made its first flight at Glendale. Performance was even better than predicted, with top speed in excess of 322 km/h (200 mph) and a range of 1,610 km (1,000 miles). Cord was delighted; he not only at once purchased a V-1 executive model for his own use, but in March 1934 announced a major re-equipment programme for American Airlines – centred on the new V-1 – which cost $2,000,000, then a very considerable sum for a new fleet. While these were delivered, Vultee improved the breed into the 735 hp-engined V-1A, which in early 1935 began putting his name on the map with a succession of point-to-point records.

One of the greatest record flights was the first crossing of the United States in under 12 hours. On 14 January 1935 Major Jimmy Doolittle, with his wife and another passenger, set out from Burbank, California, in pitch darkness and foul weather. He had to fly blind for the entire distance and severe crosswinds blew him far off track down to Richmond, Virginia, the final 7 hours being with no radio communication. Doolittle nevertheless landed at Floyd Bennett field, New York, well inside the previous record with a time of 11 hours 59 minutes at an average speed of 351 km/h (218 mph). It is extremely unlikely that any other aircraft in the world could have equalled this.

The most famous V-1A was *Lady Peace*, built for famous pilot Dick Merrill and entertainer Harry Richman. Some 40,000 ping-pong balls were carried in the wings to provide flotation in the event of ditching on a double

The Vultee Valiant was the USAAF's standard basic trainer in World War II and also served with US Navy training units. Over 11,500 were built in two main versions, the BT-13 having the 450 hp Pratt & Whitney R-985 Wasp Junior and the BT-15 being powered by the Wright R-975 Whirlwind

Atlantic crossing in 1936. However, they were not needed and the flight was successfully accomplished. By this time many operators were using the speedy Vultees. The longest single V-1A flight, with four refuelling stops, was made from Los Angeles to Moscow via the Arctic.

In 1935 the US Department of Commerce suddenly destroyed V-1A sales prospects by decreeing that no single-engined transport could fly on American scheduled routes. Though sporadic export sales of the V-1 continued, Vultee had to produce a replacement aircraft with the utmost haste. Wisely deciding that the DC-3 was too good to compete with, he instead used the wing and most other major parts of the V-1A in the V-11 attack bomber. This was quickly designed in the autumn of 1935 and flown at Glendale in October that year.

Success abroad

For its day as advanced and trim as the V-1A had been, the V-11 was a great success from the start. Its slim fuselage accommodated a crew of two or three and had a long 'greenhouse' canopy of the kind later to become common. The tailplane was moved to the top of the fuselage and positioned well ahead of the fin, while the castoring tail-wheel was faired into a small underfin. No less than 1,360 kg (3,000 lb) of bombs could be carried under and within the deep wing, and there were four machine guns in the wing all firing ahead. A fifth gun was aimed from the rear cockpit and, when a bombardier was carried, he aimed a sixth gun from a retractable lower rear position. Standard engine was the Wright R-1820 Cyclone with ratings from 710 hp to 1,000 hp. Deliveries began in mid-1936 to Turkey (40), China (30) and Brazil (26).

The Soviet Union purchased several different sub-types and subsequently constructed a very small number. A report then circulated that the V-11 had been adopted by Japan and in 1942 a British journal published complete details of the 'Showa SB-99', said to be one of the most important attack bombers of the Imperial Army (and widely reported by Allied pilots, who knew it by the Allied code-name Millie). In fact all this was mistaken and no V-11 ever reached Japan. After Vultee had completed most orders, the US Air Corps finally bought seven V-11A and V-11G sub-types for service testing as the YA-19. The V-11A had the 1,600 hp R-2600 Cyclone 14 and a speed raised from some 369 km/h (229 mph) to 451 km/h (280 mph). Sadly, Gerard Vultee never lived to see the white star on his aircraft, for he died with his wife in an air crash in Arizona in 1938.

In 1936 the Vultee company's big orders forced the construction of wholly-new and much larger facilities. Vultee Field was established at Downey, in those days a village well outside Los Angeles, and a plant was built which grew for nine consecutive years. Here was built the V-12 family, designated immediately after Vultee's death by Richard Palmer. A cleaned-up and refined V-11, the V-12 had a 0.5 in and a 0.3 in gun in each wing, one of each calibre in the cowling and two 0.3 in guns in the rear cockpit – 27 times the fire-power of the contemporary Fairey Battle. China bought 26 V-12C aircraft and 52 examples of the speedy V-12D with the R-2600 engine.

Multi-role design

Airplane Development became the Vultee Aircraft Division in 1938, and operated as a subsidiary of an independent Avco (Aviation Corporation). Chief designer Palmer and board chairman Harry Woodhead agreed on a possibly unique project: to use basically the same design for all kinds of aircraft from a basic trainer to a fighter.

The objective was a gigantic reduction in man-hours and cost, aided by the installation at Downey of the world's first powered assembly line for aircraft, similar to that long familiar in the car industry. Common tooling was to be used whenever possible. Though the inevitable outcome was a series of compromises, biased heavily in favour of the fighter, the result was most successful. The greatest success was the basic trainer, despite the fact it had a symmetrical-aerofoil wing designed for a high-performance fighter.

The four basic models were the P-48 fighter, BC-51 basic combat, B-54 advanced trainer and B-54D basic trainer. In general, all had the same wing, rear fuselage and tail, while other parts were common to a surprising degree. Construction was all-metal, with stressed-skin used throughout except over the centre section, which was a steel-tube structure covered with quick-release panels for access. All four designs were completed by the end of 1938.

The P-48 was a trim single-seater with a 1,200 hp Pratt & Whitney Twin Wasp S4C4-G radial engine. At the time of its first flight on 9 September 1939, the prototype featured an engine beautifully-cowled in a pointed nose

Top: the V-1A high-speed airliner made several notable record-breaking flights, including a crossing of the United States in under 12 hours. Above: mechanics work on a Vultee Model 48 Vanguard fighter trainer

Vultee Vengeance Mark 1A of No 21 Squadron, Royal Australian Air Force

Dimensions
Span 14·64 m (48 ft)
Length 12·12 m (39 ft 6 in)
Height 5·58 m (15 ft 4 in)

Engine
One 1,700 hp Wright
Cyclone R-2600-A5B

Performance
Maximum speed 448 km/h (279 mph)
at 4,000 m (13,000 ft)
Service ceiling 6,800 m (22,300 ft)
Range 3,700 km (2,300 miles)

Armament
Four fixed forward-firing and two flexibly-
mounted 0·3 in machine guns
910 kg (2,000 lb) of bombs

which in fact did little for the aircraft except make proper engine cooling difficult. Named Vanguard, the fighter was basically good, although not in the class of its contemporary, the Focke Wulf Fw 190. With a conventional cowling, the second prototype reached the excellent speed of 576 km/h (358 mph) and in February 1940 Sweden ordered 144 examples, each with two 12·7 mm guns in the fuselage and four 7·62 mm weapons in the wing. Deliveries were to begin in September 1941, but the US Government had by this time banned war exports to Sweden. Britain agreed to take 100 Vanguards, but only the first two were evaluated in RAF markings. The whole batch was eventually allocated to China, together with 29 others, all designated Vultee 48C, while the remaining 15 went to West Coast USAAF bases as fighter trainers, with the designation P-66.

Valiant basic trainer

In contrast, the B-54D was a great success. In 1939 the Army Air Corps ordered 300 as the BT-13 Valiant, following with an order for another 500 in 1940. Vultee Field's assembly line not only flew the first BT-13 just 88 days after

the order, but went on to increase output until the total production for the single month of June 1943 exceeded that of Vultee's first nine years (1932-41). The eventual total was 11,537 and the Valiant was in all respects a thoroughly likeable, tough and serviceable machine. There were various sub-types designated BT-13, BT-13A and BT-15 by the USAAF and SNV-1 and SNV-2 by the US Navy, but all had fixed landing gear, tandem cockpits with greenhouse canopy and slotted hydraulic flaps. Standard engine was the 450 hp Wasp Junior, driving a Hamilton two-position propeller, but the BT-15 had a Wright Whirlwind. Small numbers of the 'basic combat' model, which became the Valiant 51 used by the USAAF as the BC-3, were built. This had a 550 hp Wasp and retractable landing gear, and, unlike the very similar AT-6 family which in US service were usually unarmed, it had a fixed gun for the pilot and a second weapon aimed from the rear cockpit.

In 1940 Vultee took over the Stinson Company and on 19 December 1941 Avco, the parent, took over the big Consolidated Aircraft concern. The companies were formally amalgamated in March 1943 as Consolidated

Vultee Aircraft, subsequently abbreviated to Convair. Expansion was tremendous and Vultee Field Division was supported by the gigantic Nashville Division, which had originally been Stinson's airliner plant. Another Convair division at Miami made parts for Vultee as well as for the Consolidated B-24, Lockheed P-38 and Vought F4U.

The RAF's Stuka

Vultee's chief wartime combat type was the Vengeance dive bomber. This began as the Model 72, designed to a British specification in 1940 by Palmer. It was expected to be the RAF's equivalent of the Junkers Ju 87 Stuka, but by 1941 the dive bomber was considered too vulnerable to operate over Western Europe. This was a short-sighted view and the Vengeance was not used to the full except by the RAF in Burma, where in 1943–44 it proved extremely valuable. The Royal Australian Air Force also operated the type in the South-West Pacific.

The typical Vultee stressed-skin, clean design was maintained in the Vengeance, though the cranked wing planform made some observers think (wrongly) that the aircraft's centre of gravity had given problems. Power was provided by a 1,600 hp Cyclone R-2600-19 or 1,700 hp R-2600-17, with broad paddle-blade Hamilton propeller. Pilot and observer sat in tandem, while a bomb-bay under the centre-section spars could accommodate four 500 lb bombs. The proposed TBV-1 version for the US Navy was designed to carry two torpedoes, but the type was not built. The main undercarriage legs retracted rearwards into the centre section and the wing outer panels carried upper and lower hydraulic dive-brakes, which were very effective.

The British Purchasing Commission bought 700 Vengeances 'off the drawing board', but the March 1941 Lend-Lease Act resulted in a complex production situation. Eventually 1,731 were built, Convair Nashville delivering 500 Vengeance Mk II, 100 Lend-Lease Mk III, 100 A-35A and 831 A-35B aircraft, while Northrop built 200 Mk I and Lend-Lease Mk IA Vengeances. The Mark I, II and III had the R-2600-19 engine and British armament and equipment, including four 0·303 in wing guns and two more in the rear cockpit. At least 243 of various British marks went to the USAAF as the A-31. The A-35 was an American version with the R-2600-13 or R-2600-17 engine, four 0·5 in wing guns and a fifth in the rear cockpit; the A-35B had six wing guns. Altogether, 562 American Vengeances, a mix of A-35As and Bs, went to the RAF and RAAF as the Vengeance Mk IV. The final 29 off the Nashville line went to Brazil at the close of production in September 1944.

The name Vultee was often applied to the Stinson-designed O-49/L-1 Vigilant STOL observation machine, 324 production examples having been built at the Vultee Nashville plant. Vultee also produced two families of startlingly unconventional fighters during World War II, though neither was produced. The XP-54 was built to a 1940 Army Air Corps specification and was a giant twin-boom pusher-engined type, powered by a 2,300 hp Lycoming XH-2470. The pilot got into his lowered seat at ground level and was then winched electrically up into the pressurised cockpit, the lower closure forming a pressure-tight seal. In emergency the seat ejected downwards. In the nose were two 37 mm T-9 cannon and two 0·5 in machine guns. The other oddity was the XP-81, produced under the Convair name at Downey and flown at Muroc (later Edwards AFB) by Frank Davis, then Vultee chief engineer and later president of Convair. The XP-81, flown in February 1945, had a Packard Merlin in the nose

The Vultee Vengeance was the only dive-bomber to serve operationally with the Royal Air Force, four front-line squadrons being equipped with the type in India. No 82 Squadron was the first, re-equipping with Vengeances in August 1942. However, it was No 110 Squadron which flew the first dive-bombing sortie with the type, when a Japanese headquarters was attacked on 19 March 1943. In December 1942 two more units, Nos 45 and 84 Squadrons, converted onto Vengeances.

Top: a total of 1,125 BT-13B trainers were built. They differed from earlier models in having a 24-volt electrical system. Above: the Vengeance dive bomber saw little service with the USAAF, although it was flown operationally by the RAF and the Royal Australian Air Force in the Far East

and Allison J33 turbojet in the tail. In December 1945 came the YP-81, in which the nose engine was a General Electric XT31 turboprop. The idea was long-endurance escort, cruising on the propeller, with jet power added for combat, when 829 km/h (515 mph) could be attained. However, the USAAF cancelled the 13 service-test aircraft. Vultee Field had meanwhile started a thriving missile programme, which led to Convair's Terrier family. This moved to Pomona in 1947, when Downey closed and the Vultee name vanished.

The Reich's Revenge

Nazi Germany's dreaded V1 and V2 weapons brought a dramatic twist to the closing stages of the war in Europe

The German experimental station at Peenemünde, planned in 1935, was opened in April 1937. Here, on a tongue of land jutting out into the Baltic, 96 km (60 miles) north-west of Stettin, a team of scientists headed by Werner von Braun devised rocket weapons under the direction of General Walter Dornberger. Von Braun's main interest was space exploration, fostered at first as a matter of national prestige, but when war came rockets were seen by the Nazis as possible long-range artillery. Early experiments had limited success until the A-4 type gyroscopically-stabilised, finned rocket reached a height of 85 km (53 miles) on 3 October 1942.

When a pulse-jet-powered flying bomb was projected by Argus Motorenwerke, and developed by Fieseler as their Fi 103, it was sent to Peenemünde for proving as the FZG76 (Fernzielgerät or long-range target apparatus). Early experimental fuselages of December 1942 were air-launched from a Focke Wulf Fw 200 and in July 1943 a 246 km (153 miles) ground-launched flight with good accuracy encouraged further development. It was this bomb that the Germans called their V1 (Vergeltungswaffe 1 or reprisal weapon 1) and placed it in large-scale production at the Volkswagen works at Fallersleben.

Trial launches

To operate the V1, a new unit, designated Flak Regiment 155W, was formed under Colonel M. Wachtel. Trial launches were started at Zempin, a village near Peenemünde, before moving to Northern France where sites for the storage and launching of flying bombs were being prepared. Plans were made to launch the V1 attack late in 1943 with 1,000 missiles a day dispatched from a series of small sites holding 20 and large sites with storage space for 250.

As early as November 1939 British intelligence had been warned of rocket experiments at Peenemünde in a document delivered to the British Embassy in Oslo. Interrogation of German prisoners and escaped Polish nationals gave credence to reports of German experiments with long-range missiles. Photographic reconnaissance failed to attain any significant evidence until, quite by chance during a sortie in a Spitfire on 15 May 1942 to Swinemünde, Flight Lieutenant D. W. Steventon detected an airfield and activity near the mouth of the River Peene and set his cameras in motion. From then on the area was kept under periodic surveillance.

As a result of the intelligence collected, Air Marshal

A Hawker Tempest Mk V closes upon its prey, a V1 flying bomb, over Southern England. Only the the fastest fighters, such as the Tempest, North American P-51, Republic P-47 and Supermarine Spitfire Mk XIV could be used to intercept the fast-flying V1s

Left: the RAF Bomber Command night attack on the Peenemünde experimental station on 17/18 August 1943 seriously disrupted V1 testing. Centre: a V1 seen after launching. Numbers of V1s were also air-launched from Heinkel He 111s. Bottom: a painting by L. Cole depicts a V1 shot down by anti-aircraft fire while another flies on. About half the V1s successfully launched were brought down

Harris ordered Operation Hydra, in which a force of 600 bombers made an attack on Peenemünde on the night of 17/18 August, in full moon to permit accurate location of the dispersed buildings set in woodland. Because the target route was similar to that of recent Berlin raids, a diversionary attack on the German capital was carried out that night by de Havilland Mosquitoes. A few aircraft were forced to abort and 597 heavy bombers set out. The recently-introduced master bomber technique was used and its success was enhanced by an early identification of the target area before the smoke screen defences had time to take effect. Among the 27 buildings completely destroyed was the senior officers mess and a key scientist was killed. By the time the bombers were returning, however, the German fighter controller had deployed his night fighters and in the bright moonlight some 30 bombers were shot down; a total of 41 was lost.

The raid seriously affected V-weapon proving, but building work continued on the launching sites in France. Soon photo-reconnaissance of Northern France revealed a series of ski-shaped erections, confirmed by intelligence from French resistance at some 80 locations, all placed at a distance of 217km (135 miles) from London. Photographic interpreters, among whom was Constance Babington Smith of the Women's Auxiliary Air Force, detected a small type of aircraft at some of the sites; both the aircraft and the site shapes linked with photographs taken over Peenemünde. The signs were ominous and defensive measures were planned under the code-name 'Crossbow', the code-word 'Diver' being allotted to the V1 weapon itself.

'Noball' targets

Attacks by RAF heavy bombers and Martin Marauder medium bombers of the US Ninth Air Force on the launching and supply sites, code-named 'Noball' targets, started on 20 December 1943 and, from Christmas Eve onwards, were joined by 'heavies' of the US Eighth Air Force. Between April and June, RAF Bomber Command, committed both to invasion preparation and support work and maintaining its offensive against German towns, devoted thirteen per cent of its total effort against flying bomb supply and launching sites, suffering the loss of 38 aircraft.

A week after D-day, in the early hours of 13 June 1944, the first V1 rockets were launched against south-east England. Observer Corps M2 post members made the first 'Diver' sighting, while other less well-informed individuals reported objects coming in over the sea trailing flames and sounding like two-stroke motorcycles. The first of the four V1s crossing the coast fell at Swanscombe, Kent, while one reached London to hit a railway bridge at Bethnal Green, killing six people. Then came a short lull, due to German inability to sustain the attack. However, two nights later the onslaught began in earnest. Immediately Air Marshal Sir Roderic Hill, commanding Air Defence Great Britain, put his anti-Diver plans into operation. Barrage balloon squadrons were re-deployed to form a screen to the south of London stretching from

Leatherhead in Surrey to Gravesend in Kent. Further south, anti-aircraft batteries took up new positions along the North Downs, while along the coastal strip and out to sea fighters had free range.

For the fighters, tackling pilotless aircraft flying up to 644 km/h (400 mph) posed new problems. Spitfire Mark XIVs and Tempest Mark Vs of the six squadrons initially allotted to the anti-Diver role were modified to achieve extra speed; armour was removed since there was no retaliatory fire, and, in some cases, paint was removed and surfaces were polished to reduce drag. To close in, fire and destroy the V1, meant pilots risking destruction in the explosion. Causing bombs to fall short of the metropolis by other means and explode in the sea or rural areas was also effective. With this in mind on 23 June, a Spitfire pilot tipped a V1 over by drawing level and edging nearer to flip its wing with his own wingtip. Four days later a Tempest, with the advantage of height to aid its speed, overtook a V1, causing it to dive out of control in the air turbulence of the Tempest's slipstream. Soon pilots were using all three methods and Spitfire Marks IX and XII, Hawker Typhoon day fighters and Mosquito night

fighters joined the fray.

In spite of the defences' joint endeavours, about half the 'Doodle-bugs', as the V1s were colloquially known to the public, succeeded in reaching London. They wrought terrible havoc; the bombs, set on course from their launching ramp, came down when their carefully-measured fuel gave out. Diving to earth, their 850 kg warhead of Trialen exploded on contact, reducing buildings in the immediate vicinity to rubble and causing damage over a wide radius. By mid-July, some 4,000 civilians had been killed by the weapons and many others injured.

Anti-aircraft defences

A desperate measure was taken on 17 July, effecting a change of defence planning and another massive redeployment. The bulk of the guns of General Sir Frederick Pile's Anti-Aircraft Command were moved to the coast, giving better visual approach conditions and uncluttered radar responses. Some of the defences had been placed to shield Bristol from attack from launching sites in the Cherbourg area but, as the Allies overran the latter area, an even greater density of guns could be ranged between St

Top left: a Supermarine Spitfire employs one of the methods of destroying a V1 – putting it out of control by tipping its wing to upset its gyroscope.
Top: a V1 launch site (marked A), in the Pas de Calais, following an Allied attack. B to E indicate where V1s crashed on launching.
Above: a painting by J. B. Stafford-Baker depicts a V2 transport train destroyed near Oyle by Second Tactical Air Force aircraft.
Above left: a technician makes an adjustment to a V2 before it is launched against Britain

Margaret's Bay, Kent, and Beachy Head, Sussex. Soon the guns, using proximity fuses, were shooting down more V1s than the fighters.

With their fiery tails, V1s were easy to locate in the dark and the fighter offensive, directed in lanes to avoid the areas of massed guns, continued day and night. A flight of North American Mustang Mk IIIs of No 316 (Polish) Squadron were assigned to the anti-Diver task and proved so effective that a Mustang wing of the Second Tactical Air Force was brought in. The first of the RAF's jet units, No 616 Squadron, became operational from 14 July and their Gloster Meteor Mk Is shot down 13 V1s. Mosquito squadrons were also placed on anti-Diver patrols; Sqn Ldr Francis R. L. Mellersh of No 98 Squadron achieved the record of nine V1 kills in a single sortie. Several pilots lost their lives firing on V1s, among them Commandant Jean-Marie Maridor DFC serving with No 91 Squadron RAF; he died in the explosion of his 11th kill.

During the evening of 2 August 1944 a squadron of P-51D Mustangs of the 4th Fighter Group USAAF attacked a train detected in a siding at Remy, while another squadron of the Group provided top cover. After strafing the heavily-camouflaged wagons there was an explosion so mighty that even the top cover aircraft rocked in its blast. Haystacks many fields away were set on fire and buildings in distant villages were damaged as a flying bomb supply train disintegrated.

From July to September, Bomber Command dropped 44,335 tons of bombs on V-weapon targets, representing twenty-five per cent of its total effort. The US Eighth Air Force made daylight attacks on Peenemünde and made 16,272 sorties against Noball targets, losing 63 B-17s and B-24s. Their Noball attack was made on 30 August but the Ninth Air Force, based on the Continent, continued their attacks into 1945.

The turning point was reached on the night of 27/28 August when, out of 97 V1s launched, only 10 slipped through to London. Then the Allied advance along the French coast caused launchings from France to cease from 2 September. Up to that time the fighters claimed 1,900 V1s destroyed, the guns 1,560 and the balloons 278. The lull was only temporary, however, for Germany continued the offensive by air-launching V1s from Heinkel He 111s operating from Dutch bases from the night of 4/5 September and from German bases in mid-September.

V2 rocket

However, by that time a more serious attack was developing for which there was no defence. After some 250 A-4 rockets had been built at Peenemünde they were put into large-scale production at a plant in the Harz Mountains as Hitler's revenge weapon, the V2 rocket. The concrete structures in France, planned as launching sites, had attracted so much attention from the Western Allies that long, mobile trailers were made to launch the 14m (46ft) rockets, with ramps to raise the rocket for launching, controlled by an attendant armoured vehicle. Final development work was transferred to Poland and rocket debris was soon in the hands of Polish partisans, who contacted British intelligence. A Douglas Dakota fitted with long-range fuel tanks, of No 267 Squadron, RAF based at Brindisi in Italy, made three trips to a secret landing ground in Poland and brought back rocket and flying bomb parts for scientific analysis.

At 1843 hours on 8 September the first two V2 rockets reached Britain. They fell simultaneously, one harmlessly

at Epping and the other at Chiswick causing 13 casualties. The launching sites were traced to The Hague district of Holland and both intruder raids and armed reconnaissance flights were made from Britain. Allied Expeditionary Force fighters based on the continent added their weight to strafing attacks, particularly along the supply lines. Due to Allied advances the launching positions were withdrawn to Friesland and directed towards Norwich. After the Allied check at Arnhem, however, sites were again moved

forward to The Hague to bring London within the 320km (200 mile) range capability of the rockets. These reached a maximum speed of 5,580km/h (3,467mph), levelled off and descended vertically at such speed that there was virtually no warning. Their 975kg (2,145lb) warheads, composed mainly of amatol, caused large craters. One hit a large store by New Cross Gate station in south-east London on 25 November, killing 160 people and seriously injuring over a hundred more. Later, a hit on a block of flats at Stepney killed 134 people outright.

Sporadic attacks by air-launched V1s continued, the most determined effort being made the night before Christmas Eve when Heinkel He 111s crossed the coast to direct 30 V1s to Manchester; only one reached the target area. Among the defensive measures taken was a new gun strip along the East Anglian coast with offshore patrols carried out by Mosquitoes. The last air-launch against Britain was made on 7 January 1945, but this was not the last of the bombs. Three launching sites were made in Holland for use with increased-range V1s and of the 125 launched, 13 reached London. The majority were claimed by Anti-aircraft Command, naval gunners on warships accounting for two.

Because of the difficulties in reaching London, the Germans turned the weight of their V-weapon attacks against Antwerp in an effort to stop the Allies using the port facilities. By this time there was a quick reaction by Allied Expeditionary Air Forces fighters, from a watch kept on V2 launchings; furthermore rocket fuel was becoming scarce due to continuous pounding by Allied aircraft along railways, roads and canals.

The last V2 to reach Britain fell at Orpington, Kent on 27 March. By that time 517 had fallen on London, 537 in other parts of the country and 58 were reported exploded at sea; others had exploded in the air. Two days later the last of some 9,000 V1s operationally launched reached England. Many had failed on launching sites or disappeared into the sea. The United Kingdom defences reported 6,725 approaching and recorded 5,233 coming overland. Altogether the V-weapons which fell on Britain killed 8,994 people and injured 24,504.

A V2 captured by Allied forces in France is pictured on display in Trafalgar Square in 1945. The British were defenceless against the V2 which approached from great height and faster than the speed of sound. However, too few were launched to produce the devastation and panic hoped for by Adolf Hitler

Sedans of the Air

The Waco Aircraft Company was America's largest lightplane manufacturer in the inter-war years

The immediate postwar years would seem to be an inopportune period in which to launch an aircraft manufacturing company. It was despite the almost total cutback in military procurement and the failure of several previously-flourishing firms that the Advance Aircraft Company commenced trading in the town of Troy, Ohio in 1921. With so many de Havilland, Thomas-Morse, Standard and Curtiss machines to be had for a pittance, the concern determined to provide an aircraft which would set new standards in manoeuvrability, speed and payload. The latter was a vitally important consideration, since the majority of the war-surplus types available barely accommodated the two occupants they had been designed to carry.

By 1926, production of the Waco 9 had been established at a rate of ten aircraft a week, with increased manufacturing space being acquired during that year. The Waco 9 was a three-seat biplane of conventional appearance. For economy's sake, it was powered by a 90 hp Curtiss OX-5 engine which, as it was also the ubiquitous Curtiss Jenny's power plant, was easily obtained. The type's fuselage was of tubular steel construction and fabric-covered, while the wings were wood. The Waco 9 was advertised at the competitive price of 2,600 dollars, boasted a maximum speed of 148 km/h (92 mph) and had an endurance of five hours.

The Advance Aircraft Company decided in 1929 to take the name of its product, becoming the Waco Aircraft Company in June of that year. The name itself was an acronym, derived from the initials of a previous concern, the Weaver Aircraft Company. By this time, the Waco 9 had been refined through the short-lived Waco 10 to become what was simply known as the Waco Three-seat Biplane. Offered with a variety of engines ranging from the original OX-5 to the mighty 300 hp Wright Whirlwind, the Three-seat Biplane proved a resounding success.

Although still similar to the Waco 9, the higher-powered versions of the Three-seat Biplane were available with a choice of parallel or tapered wings. The company boasted at this time that the 220 hp Wright-engined variant with tapered wings had 'won every contest in which it has been entered'. Distinguishable by the 'N' struts supporting the upper wing centre-section, the type retained the radiator slung from the leading edge above the pilot's head which had been a feature of the Waco 9.

The year 1932 saw three types being marketed, designated the Models A, C and F. The Model A bore some of the hallmarks better associated with American automobile design, the most notable of which was a 'coupe' hardtop cover which could be used to convert the open-cockpit biplane to an enclosed type. Dual controls were standard, while a large luggage locker was situated in the aft fuselage. The Model C four-seat cabin biplane featured automobile-type triangular 'side-light' windows, but otherwise differed considerably from the Model A. A cluttered-looking aeroplane with a multiplicity of interplane struts and bracing wires, this 'sedan of the air' had a cruise range of 700 km (435 miles) at a speed of up to 214 km/h (133 mph) in the 210 hp Kinner-engined version.

The celebrated Three-seat biplane had now become known as the Model F. Retaining many of its ancestor's features, but with certain added refinements including a tailwheel, the Model F was to become the most successful of the company's products. Like the Models A and C, the

The Waco 10 was one of the first products of the fledgling Advance Aircraft Company in the late 1920s. Developed from the earlier, highly-successful Waco 9, the type featured a new, fully-enclosed engine cowling, balanced differential ailerons and a redesigned undercarriage. Both the Waco 10 and its successor, the Three-seat Biplane, inspired the Waco Model F, the company's most successful product of the 1930s

Model F utilised the standard Waco wooden wing, with spruce spars, spruce-and-plywood ribs and fabric covering married to a steel-tube fabric-covered fuselage. All types were available with a choice of engines, thus giving rise to designations such as RBA and UBA for the Model A, OEC, UEC and BEC for the Model C and CPF, KNF and UPF for the three-seater.

The Waco Aircraft Company had maintained a steady growth relative to its rivals throughout the 1920s and had successfully survived the Great Depression of the early 1930s. It was a matter of some pride, therefore, when the company was described in the mid-1930s as being 'the largest producer of commercial aircraft in the United States of America'. Indeed, during the mid-1920s, the company's output had exceeded that of all other commercial aircraft producers combined. A prodigious sales network had been set up, which in 1935 consisted of 55 distributors, 175 dealers in the US and representatives in 25 foreign countries, including territories as disparate as China, Germany and New Zealand. All production models were optionally available in seaplane configuration, equipped with twin Edo floats.

The Model C remained in production in 1935, but was joined in the Waco line by the Model C Custom. As the name implied, the latter was a 'de luxe' version of the basic aircraft, featuring electrically-operated flaps on the upper wing, a larger baggage compartment, aileron trim tabs for easier handling and updated equipment. Engines now available ranged from the 210 hp Continental R-670 to the 250 hp Wright Whirlwind radial. The faithful Model F was still on offer with the designation Waco F-5. Appearing alongside the Models C and F in the Waco range in 1939 was the ungainly Model N. Although a token concession to modernity, a tricycle undercarriage gave the type a peculiar appearance and was somewhat at variance with the simple, yet graceful lines of its sister aircraft. Potential customers must evidently have agreed with this assessment, for the type saw only limited production by Waco standards.

Military developments

With the exception of a single Waco 9 ordered by the US Army in the Fiscal Year 1926, no Waco aircraft had been ordered by the military services. In an effort to remedy this situation, the Model D was introduced. A single-bay staggered biplane with a faired undercarriage, the type seated pilot and observer/gunner in tandem. The Model D was unusual in that the upper wing was supported by a strut which met the fuselage in the pilot's line of vision. Landing lights, flares and blind-flying instrumentation were standard, while armament consisted of two 0·3 in Browning machine guns in the lower wing, a similar weapon being wielded by the observer at the rear. The type was advertised as being able to perform no less than 12 military functions; these included fighter, bomber, observation post, photographic aircraft, mailplane, ambulance, trainer and seaplane. A number of aircraft served with the air arm of Uruguay in the late 1930s and

In many respects the archetypal Waco biplane, the Model F was produced in greater numbers and with a greater variety of power plants than any of its sister aircraft. Many examples of the Model F have been restored and are still flying, over 45 years after the type was first introduced

Below: continuing Waco's successful policy of improvement and refinement of existing types, the Model S was one of the company's final peacetime designs. Owing much to the automobile-like Model C, the Model S performed well. Bottom: a Waco CG-4A Hadrian named 'Voo-Doo' became the first glider to cross the Atlantic by air in mid-1943. The Hadrian was towed from Montreal, Canada to Prestwick in Scotland by a twin-engined Douglas Dakota transport

early 1940s, but the advent of the monoplane was quickly to render the type obsolete.

Despite the lack of quantity orders from the military, several Waco aircraft were bought 'off the shelf' by the US Navy. Two Model F biplanes were delivered in 1934 as XJW-1 utility aircraft for the airship USS *Macon*. These aircraft were fitted with hooks above the wing centre-section to enable them to engage a 'trapeze' device on the airship, a concept taken further operationally by the Curtiss F9C-2 Sparrowhawk fighter. The *Macon* crashed in February 1935, however, and the Model F's employment was thus necessarily brief. The US Coast Guard acquired three Model C cabin biplanes in 1936, operating the type as the J2W-1; three further aircraft were impressed from private owners shortly after America's entry into World War II.

In addition to its limited naval service, the Model F was evaluated by the US Army Air Corps in 1939, together with the St Louis PT-1W, in an effort to find a new primary

trainer. Thirteen PT-14 aircraft, as they became known, followed the 220hp Continental-engined trials machine into service, another example impressed in wartime becoming the sole PT-14A. Waco's final peacetime assault on the general aviation market came with the Model E five-seat cabin biplane.

Representing the company's most luxuriously appointed product to date, the Model E's specification included a tailwheel, cabin heaters and ventilators, a streamlined NACA cowling enclosing the Jacobs, Pratt & Whitney or Wright engine and a large baggage area. Twin seats at the front were provided with a 'throw-over' control yoke, by which control could be transferred in flight: a rear bench seat accommodated three. With a 420hp Wright R975E-3 engine, the aircraft was designated the Waco WRE: maximum speed with this power plant was 330km/h (204mph). The Model F was marketed as a trainer with its seating reduced to two, and remained in production until the Japanese raid on Pearl Harbour. The Model S was reminiscent in configuration of the Model C of the mid-1930s, but with a 250hp Continental engine had a superior top speed of 234km/h (145mph).

The Waco Aircraft Company devoted the years from August 1941 to August 1945 entirely to the fulfilment of military contracts. A total of 44 Waco lightplanes of varying marks was impressed into US Army service with the blanket designation of UC-72, but the majority of Waco's war effort was represented by the four gliders which bore its name. Few examples of the CG-3A troop training glider were built, but the 15-seat CG-4A which followed proved to be both the first and the most widely-used US troop glider of the war.

Haig and Hadrian

Named Haig in US service and Hadrian by the Royal Air Force, over 20,400 were built by 15 American manufacturers. The type was first used operationally in the Allied invasion of Sicily in July 1943; a few weeks previously, a Hadrian in RAF markings had become the first glider to cross the Atlantic by air, being towed from Montreal to Britain by a Douglas C-47. The CG-13A was a large 42-seat cargo and troop glider of Waco design which was built by the Northwestern Aeronautical Corporation and the Ford Motor Company, while the CG-15A was a refinement of the CG-4A. A total of 427 of the former was delivered.

The prevailing economic climate in postwar years was as uncertain as that in which the company had been founded a quarter-century previously. With a history of biplane manufacture, Waco was ill-equipped to compete in a market in which the monoplane now held sway. Nevertheless, a challenging project, named the Aristocraft, was unveiled in 1946; it was a four-seat high-wing cabin monoplane, with a 215hp Franklin engine in the nose driving a pusher propeller at the rear. No rudder bar was provided, the ailerons and twin rudders being linked. The prototype flew in March 1947 and deliveries of the retractable-undercarriage type were scheduled to begin later that year.

In June, however, only three months after first flight, development was abandoned. Company president Clayton J. Brukner announced that, due to delays in the engineering and construction of the prototype, together with the need for unexpected further development and the uncertainty of future markets, the Aristocraft was to be Waco's last design, 'at least until 1950'. Sadly, the abandonment of the project was to write the closing line in the story of America's oldest commercial aircraft manufacturer for all time.

Rebel Recce Pilot

Despite his unconventional methods, Adrian Warburton proved one of the RAF's top photo-reconnaissance exponents

Adrian Warburton was one of the many young men who left their employment – in his case, the world of banking – to join the Royal Air Force as World War II loomed in 1938. Aged 19, Warburton was accepted for pilot training and was granted a short-service commission. His first posting was to No 608 Squadron, then flying the twin-engined Blackburn Botha on patrols over the North Sea from Thornaby, Yorkshire. No one thought much of the underpowered Botha, least of all Warburton who was soon 'carpeted' by his commanding officer for his lack of affinity with his aircraft. The Squadron's loss was to be Malta's gain for, exasperated by Warburton's treatment of the Botha, the squadron commander recommended him for a transfer to fill an observer's vacancy which had arisen in the Mediterranean.

Temporarily suspended from duties as a pilot, Warburton sat and passed the general reconnaissance course and navigated a Martin Maryland to Malta, by way of Gibraltar. If the grey mists of the North Sea had quelled the spirit and dulled the abilities, the warm Mediterranean sun brought a transformation. Within four days of arrival he was navigating his Maryland on operational flights, and a week later had been reinstated as a pilot.

Warburton then undertook his first major operation. He was briefed to make the final pre-strike reconnaissance of Taranto harbour on 10 November 1940 preparatory to the Fleet Air Arm's torpedo attack on the Italian navy. Flying his lone Maryland at low level in bad weather, he surprised the Italian defences and proceeded to circle inside the enemy harbour twice, operating the camera while his navigator read the names of the vessels off their hulls and plotted them on his map. When at last the Italian ground defences opened fire, Warburton withdrew for a few minutes before returning for yet another run over the target. His photographs and notes were rushed to HMS *Illustrious*, whose Swordfish crews were thus provided with minute detail of their target; the result was that on the night of 11/12 November they put three Italian battleships, a cruiser and a destroyer out of action.

Living legend

Warburton was one of the original members of No 431 (Long Range Reconnaissance) Flight established under Squadron Leader E. A. Whiteley at Luqa to provide essential reconnaissance in the Central Mediterranean. The job of the Maryland crews – soon formed into No 69 Squadron – was vital in locating enemy ships plying between the Italian ports and the Axis armies in North Africa, a job made more hazardous with the arrival in strength of the Luftwaffe on Sicily in early 1941. Nor was the task simply a matter of locating harmless merchantmen; towards the end of 1941 Warburton came upon a convoy of four transports escorted by two battleships, two cruisers and fifteen destroyers steaming under a veritable umbrella of Ju 88s. However, once again he escaped with the vital news.

Warburton was by now a living legend on the gallant island. Recognising that he possessed an extraordinary determination and ability, Malta's AOC, Air Vice-Marshal

Left: pictured when a flight lieutenant, Adrian Warburton swiftly attained the rank of wing commander despite his unorthodoxy.
Below: Warburton on the wing of an American Lockheed Lightning, the type in which he was to disappear without trace in April 1944

Hugh Lloyd forgave and tolerated the pilot's many eccentricities. Warburton's recognition of danger simply did not exist; although the guns of the Maryland were intended strictly for its protection, 'Warby' could seldom resist the temptation to use them otherwise. On one occasion, while photographing airfields in Sicily, he found himself at low level over the enemy airfield at Catania; putting his wheels down, he received a 'green' to land, but then proceeded to launch a withering attack on the parked enemy aircraft, leaving two Junkers Ju 52/3m transports and two Savoia-Marchetti SM 79s in flames.

Personal Beaufighter

In air combat he was no less aggressive and his score of air victories rose to eleven, about half of them shot down while flying the Maryland. In time, however, the strain began to tell, and in December 1941 Warburton, now a Flight Lieutenant with two Distinguished Flying Crosses, was detached from Malta to Egypt. Here he was required to evaluate the Martin Baltimore shortly to replace the Marylands – but to Warby the new aircraft was just another Botha. He managed to acquire the loan of a Beaufighter which he considered to be 'the fastest aeroplane in the Mediterranean' and he proceeded to strip it of all guns and armour and fit it with cameras. Arriving back in Malta, Warburton found Lloyd fretting at the lack of news of a Luftwaffe build-up in Sicily. The next day Warburton landed his Beaufighter with complete photo cover of all Sicilian airfields taken from low level. As his AOC put it, 'he was the complete individualist, tireless, controversial, cynical and aloof, but in value beyond price. You had to let him do things his own way.'

Warburton continued to fly his Beaufighter for about a year until it was destroyed on the ground in a German raid. In 1943, promoted to the rank of wing commander and given command of No 683 Squadron, Warburton converted to the Spitfire PR Mark IV, and it was in one of these aircraft that he was shot down while flying off the Tunisian coast. He just managed to reach Bône airfield in Algeria where he was imprisoned by the French on suspicion of being a spy. After some embarrassment, however, the local French admiral had him flown to Gibraltar. Without wasting time with explanations, Warburton 'borrowed' a Spitfire and made his

Below: a US Army Air Force reconnaissance pilot familiarises Warburton with the Lightning's flying controls.
Bottom: Warburton was held in high regard by his USAAF counterparts, being awarded the American DFC

way back to Malta, via North Africa, shooting down a Junkers Ju 88 *en route*.

American collaboration

To the Americans, now flying in strength in the Mediterranean theatre, Warburton was simply larger than life. They had never seen a senior officer so casually attired in filthy grey flannels, oil-stained tunic and topped by a mop of long blond hair. By now he occasionally deigned to wear the ribbon of the Distinguished Service Order to which he soon added a bar, as well as a third DFC. In addition the Americans awarded him their DFC for his post-strike photographic work. On one occasion American onlookers were amazed to see him step out of a blazing Lockheed Lightning, which he had just crash-landed on their airfield, and get straight into another aircraft to complete the mission he had had to interrupt.

It was felt that Warburton's rapport with the Americans would provide firm collaboration with the USAAF's 3rd and 5th Photo Groups. As a result, on 1 October 1943, Adrian Warburton was given command of a new Photographic Reconnaissance Wing, specially created from Nos 680, 682 and 683 Squadrons of the RAF and No 60 Squadron of the South African Air Force.

Unfortunately, Warburton was to be seriously injured in a bad road accident in Tunis during October, and he was shipped home to England to recover. Six weeks in hospital was followed by a period of convalescence, during which time he was officially grounded by a medical board. Once more the weather in England palled, and on a furtive visit to his American friends at Mount Farm near Benson in Oxfordshire on 12 April 1944, he 'borrowed' a photo-reconnaissance Lightning and set off across enemy-occupied Europe to pay his old friends in the Mediterranean an unofficial visit. His aircraft was last seen by an American pilot over Lake Constance.

Air Marshal Sir Charles Portal, Chief of the Air Staff, talks with Wing Commander Adrian Warburton on Malta. Warburton's gallantry and success as a reconnaissance pilot, coupled with his eccentric personality, made him a living legend on the island

Zeppelin Killer

R. A. J. Warneford was the first Allied Airman to bring down a Zeppelin

The honour of being the first airman to bring down a Zeppelin in combat has often, erroneously, been bestowed upon Lieutenant William Leefe Robinson; the pilot to earn this distinction was R. A. J. Warneford. Born in Darjeeling, India on 15 October 1891, Warneford was initially educated at Simla and then England where he attended the Stratford-upon-Avon Grammar School. The Warneford family later moved to Canada, where the young man soon showed a mechanical flair and it came as no surprise to his parents when he joined the Indian Steam Navigation Company on the outbreak of World War I.

Warneford, fearing that the war might end before he got a chance to participate, wasted no time in returning to England and he joined up soon after his arrival. Headstrong and impetuous, Warneford quickly tired of the Army and 1915 saw him successfully gain his wings after pilot training in the Royal Naval Air Service. He was subsequently posted to No 2 Squadron RNAS, based at Eastchurch on the Thames estuary.

On 7 May 1915, the young airman was sent overseas to join No 1 Squadron at Dunkirk under Squadron Commander Arthúr Longmore. Warneford soon made a name for himself after several hectic sorties over enemy lines. As Dunkirk seemed an obvious target for the Germans, the motley collection of squadron aircraft was dispersed and Warneford soon found himself at Furnes, along with Lieutenant J. P. Wilson, Sub-Lieutenant J. S. Mills and Squadron Commander Spenser Grey.

Trio of airships

The Zeppelin raids on England had commenced during the early months of 1915 and Spenser Grey, together with his pilots, decided to bomb the raiders in their Belgian bases at Evere and Berchem Ste Agathe. On 7 June, Longmore received messages from the Admiralty in London that a trio of airships was returning from an attack on England. The 'Furnes Flight' was soon in action and acting upon a previously outlined plan; Warneford and Sub-Lieutenant Rose, both flying Morane L Parasol monoplanes, ascended from Furnes and made for Berchem with Mills and Wilson in their Henri Farmans heading towards Evere.

Army Zeppelin LZ37 commanded by Oberleutnant Otto von der Haegen had been in consort with LZ38 and LZ39 when they had taken off for England several hours earlier. LZ38 had aborted almost immediately from the mission with engine trouble and returned to its shed. This was to prove doubly unfortunate for the Germans as Mills and Wilson later successfully bombed the base at Evere, destroying the Zeppelin and its hangar.

A painting by Gordon Crosby depicting the destruction of Zeppelin LZ37 by Flt Lt R. A. J. Warneford at 3am on 7 June 1915. The action took place between Ghent and Brussels at an altitude of 1,800m (6,000ft). Warneford flying a Morane Type L, destroyed LZ37 with six 20lb Hales bombs. The Victoria Cross was conferred on him four days later

Separated from Rose, Warneford flew on unsure of his whereabouts and utterly alone until he picked out tiny blue exhaust flames beneath a curious elongated cloud. It was some time before the British pilot realised that the 'cloud' was in fact an airship, so impressive was its size. The Zeppelin's crew was not so easily surprised and machine guns in the gondolas quickly opened up on the small monoplane. Warneford took evasive action and

Four members of No 1 Squadron, RNAS pictured in 1915: Flt Sub-Lt J. S. Mills, Flt Lt A. W. Bigsworth, Flt Lt J. P. Wilson and Flt Lt R. A. J. Warneford. Warneford was detached to Furnes, near Dunkirk, with other pilots of No 1 Squadron including Mills and Wilson in May 1915 to intercept Zeppelins on missions to Great Britain

followed the airship out of range of its guns. It appeared to him that the Zeppelin was making for Ghent and so he followed hoping to seize his chance to overhaul it. To Warneford's amazement, the dirigible altered course and came in for attack. Every time the airman approached his quarry he was driven off by the spirited fire from its crew which forced him to descend out of range. With only six 20lb Hales bombs attached to a rudimentary under-carriage rack, Warneford realised that he could only do the Zeppelin lasting damage by getting above it.

Massive target

Von der Haegen must also have realised the tactical advantage of increased altitude and the airship began to ascend rapidly as ballast was dumped and speed increased in order to outrun its adversary. Nevertheless, Warneford eventually overtook the airship and managed to position his aircraft above the gleaming hull. A pull on the bomb toggle and six Hales bombs tumbled down towards the massive target. After what seemed an age the whole sky appeared to be torn asunder by terrifying explosions. The detonations which ripped the giant airship apart in a matter of seconds sent Warneford and his aircraft reeling;

the pilot fought to regain control and avoid the burning debris cascading all around him. In minutes the blazing wreckage collapsed on the Convent of Saint Elizabeth in the Mont-Saint-Armand area of Ghent, killing at least one nun and injuring several others. The helmsman of the stricken LZ37, Alfred Mühler, stayed with the forward gondola which, falling free, smashed through the convent and deposited the dazed German onto a nun's bed. Miraculously, he escaped with few injuries, the only survivor of the crew of ten.

Shortly after the Zeppelin exploded, Warneford found himself in trouble as the Morane's engine failed, com-pelling him to make a forced landing 56km (35 miles) behind enemy lines. It was fortunate indeed that Warne-ford had taken such an interest in mechanics as he soon located the source of the problem – a severed fuel line. He successfully managed to effect a repair with a piece of rag and a cigarette holder before swinging the Morane's propeller, diving into the cockpit as the machine rolled, and taking off into the night. After landing at Cape Griz-Nez for refuelling, Warneford eventually returned safely to Furnes where the news of LZ37's destruction had preceded him.

Untimely death

Within hours Warneford had become famous; his colleagues' adulation was swiftly followed by the award of the Victoria Cross on 11 June 1915. Six days later he was further decorated with the French Légion d'Honneur and after the presentation he went on to Buc in order to pick up a replacement Henri Farman for the squadron. At the airfield he was introduced to Henry Needham, an American reporter who pleaded to occupy the spare seat in Warneford's machine so that he could visit the Flight at Furnes and write a feature on the action. Warneford offered no objections and they set off to the airfield on the coast.

Soon after the aircraft had taken off, however, it appeared to become uncontrollable and with wings folding, it spun to the ground, tossing its unbelted occupants out in the process; both were killed. Legend has it that Warneford was still suffering the after-effects of a wild party thrown the night before, but this was never conclusively proven.

The body of Reginald Alexander John Warneford was taken to England and buried at Brompton Cemetery in London on 22 June.

Top right: the Morane Type L parasol-wing scout in which Warneford brought down Zeppelin LZ37.
Above right: Lt R. A. J. Warneford became a hero overnight but was killed in a flying accident on 17 June 1915.
Right: Warneford's victim, Zeppelin LZ37, pictured at Colonge. The Germans began to use such airships to raid England in early 1915

THE ONE THAT GOT AWAY

The only German to escape from captivity in Britain, Franz von Werra fell in combat soon afterwards

During World War II numerous Luftwaffe aircrew returned from crashes behind enemy lines in Russia, in North Africa and in Western Europe. Of those who fell over England however, only one was successful in escaping to return to his homeland. Born François Gustave de Werra, son of an impoverished nobleman at Leuk, Switzerland, in 1914, Franz von Werra–as he subsequently became–was a colourful character who impressed all who met him, both friend and foe, with his charming and engaging personality. Soon after François's birth his father's business collapsed and he was ruined.

François, the youngest of eight children, together with a sister, were adopted by an old family friend, Baroness Leina von Haber and her cavalry officer husband, going to live with them in Southern Germany. The break with the de Werra family was complete and in due course François's name was 'Germanised' to become Franz von Werra.

Frequently in conflict with the Baroness, whose marriage was breaking up during his childhood, Franz's boyhood was not a happy one and during his early teens he ran away to Hamburg. After a short period of destitution, he managed to sign on as a cabin boy on a liner sailing for New Orleans. News of his whereabouts reached the Baroness and on arrival in the United States he was returned home to his adoptive family.

Left: Franz von Werra claimed 13 victories on the Eastern Front after his escape from captivity. He is pictured in front of one of his victims, a Soviet bomber.
Below: the final resting place of von Werra's Messerschmitt Bf 109E-4 'Emil' after being shot down by a Fighter Command Spitfire on 5 September 1940

Flair for publicity

On completing his schooling in the mid-1930s, von Werra was able only to obtain casual employment until old enough to volunteer for the new Luftwaffe. Entering as a private, he successfully applied for pilot training and qualified as a fighter pilot in September 1938. Newly-commissioned as a *leutnant*, he was posted to Jagdgeschwader 3 which was just forming, soon acquiring a taste for low-level aerobatics. In June 1939 he crash-landed at Koenigsberg while low flying and injured his spine, remaining in hospital for several months afterwards.

Although von Werra was fit again by the outbreak of war, he found that no action came his way. Not until May 1940 and the German Blitzkrieg did JG 3 engage in other than minor operations. As Luftwaffe units moved forward behind the Panzers' breathtaking advance, JG 3 was well up to a succession of advanced airfields. From one of these in north-west France on 22 May, Messerschmitt Bf 109s of I and II/JG 3 were scrambled to intercept a trio of French Potez 63 bombers seen approaching their base. Lt von Werra attacked the first and shot it down in the Cambrai area, a second falling at the same time to an officer of I Gruppe. Giving chase to the third, von Werra was able to bring this down too a few minutes later, near Albert. This exploit was to gain for him the award of the Iron Cross, 2nd Class. During the further fighting over France up to the end of June 1940 he was to be credited with shooting down six more bombers, all of them British.

Well aware of the advantages of publicity in advancing his career, von Werra was to the fore in gaining interviews with press and radio and adopted as a pet a lion cub from

the Berlin Zoo. A photograph of him with this appeared in several publications during summer 1940. Promoted *oberleutnant*, he was made Adjutant of II/JG 3. On 28 August he became separated from his formation and returned to report that he had shot down a Supermarine Spitfire and then found six Hawker Hurricanes landing at an airfield. He stated that he followed these in, shot down two and probably a third, and then made several low strafing attacks, destroying five more on the ground. This exploit was the subject of a radio broadcast on 30 August, heralded as 'the greatest fighter exploit of the war so far'. It seems, however, that the aerial claims were not accepted for lack of witnesses. The citation to the award of the Knight's Cross (made in December 1940, when von Werra was already a British prisoner), while mentioning this exploit, credited him only with eight air and five ground victories in total.

Prisoner of war

On 5 September II/JG 3 was led over Southern England by Hauptmann Erich von Selle. The German fighters were 'bounced' by a number of Spitfires and von Werra's aircraft was hit. He crash-landed his Bf 109E-4 in a relatively undamaged condition, and was taken prisoner. The aircraft displayed on its tail unit victory bars denoted eight air and five ground victories. Some doubt exists over who shot von Werra down. Some sources credit Flt Lt J. T. Webster DFC, of No 41 Squadron. Webster claimed two Bf 109s shot down on this date to raise his score to $11\frac{1}{2}$, but was himself shot down and killed later in the day. However, the Australian Flt Lt P. C. Hughes DFC of

Adopted from Berlin Zoo, a lion cub named Simba became the Gruppe mascot when von Werra was appointed Adjutant of II Gruppe, Jagdgeschwader 3 in mid-1940. Flying from north-west France, von Werra had registered eight confirmed air victories at the time of his capture

No 234 Squadron was also victor over two Bf 109s on this day. He too was killed shortly after the action.

Following his capture, von Werra was taken to the RAF Interrogation Centre at Trent Park, Cockfosters, where much scorn was poured on his recorded claims of 28 August. Following interrogation, at which he gave little away, he was moved at the end of September to Prisoner of War Camp 1 at Grizedale Hall in the Lake District. Determined from the first to escape, he managed to slip over a wall during a route march on 7 October, but made little progress in the wild mountain terrain. On the 10th he was captured by two Home Guards while hiding in a sheep hut, but escaped again. He had little chance, however, and was caught again next afternoon.

In November came a move to the more secure Swanwick camp near Derby, where soon after arrival he joined with four other prisoners in a tunnelling project. After much digging and a partial collapse of the tunnel roof which nearly killed von Werra and another officer, all five got away, although four were swiftly recaptured. Posing as Captain Albert van Lott, a Dutch pilot with the RAF, von Werra stopped a train on the pretext that he had crash-landed a damaged Vickers Wellington bomber returning from a raid on Denmark. He was taken to Codnor station and RAF Hucknall, Nottinghamshire, was telephoned for transport. In the meantime he was interrogated by the local CID, who were convinced that he was genuine. The RAF was suspicious, however, and sent an armed driver to escort him. On arrival at Hucknall, he managed to slip out of the adjutant's office while his story was being checked. He had talked his way into the cockpit of a Hurricane being serviced by civilian contractors and was desperately trying to start it when arrested by the Duty Officer.

Escape from Canada

Back at Swanwick, Christmas brought the news that von Werra and his group were to be sent to Canada. On arrival in Nova Scotia, he took the opportunity to leap from the train carrying the prisoners from Halifax to the camp, his escape not being discovered until the next morning. He covered the 48 km (30 miles) to the St Lawrence river without being discovered and found it to be frozen over. Attempting to walk across at night, he was foiled by a narrow unfrozen channel near the south bank. He returned to the Canadian shore, where he found a large rowing boat which he managed to push across the ice so that he might float over to safety.

Von Werra was the third German prisoner to reach the United States, only one of the earlier pair, a U-boat crewman, having actually got back to Germany. He quickly became something of a celebrity and a figure of much controversy, receiving considerable publicity while an international diplomatic battle raged over his fate. After a few weeks, he quietly slipped across the frontier into Mexico on foot, obtained a false passport from the German embassy there and flew on home via Italy, reaching Germany in April 1941. There he provided much useful information for the Luftwaffe on RAF interrogation techniques and visited PoW camps to advise on security. He also wrote a book on his experiences which was withheld from publication for being too pro-British.

Meanwhile, however, the war against Russia began in June and news of the great air victories being achieved there set von Werra pressing for a return to action. A few weeks after the start of operations in the East, he was posted to command I/JG 53. By August he had gained 13 more victories to raise his total in the air to 21. During that month the unit was withdrawn to re-equip with the new Bf 109F and he went on leave and got married. In September I/JG 53 was posted back to the West, to the Dutch coastal area. On 25 October 1941 von Werra took off from Katwijk on a routine patrol, but his engine failed and he crashed into the North Sea, going down with his aircraft. His death occurred the same month as Udet's suicide and the accidental death of Werner Mölders and the news was withheld until November. It was then announced that von Werra had fallen in action in the East.

The victory tally on the tail of von Werra's Messerschmitt shortly after his unforeseen descent onto British soil. The five vertical arrows signify aircraft destroyed by ground strafing

Army Co-operation VC

World War 1 pilot Freddie West braved enemy scouts and ground fire on his sorties over the lines

Of the 19 airmen awarded a Victoria Cross during World War I, eight died before the Armistice. The longest-surviving air VC of the conflict was Air Commodore Ferdinand Maurice Felix West. Born in London on 29 January 1896, 'Freddie' West was the only son of an English army oficer and a French countess. When his father was killed in 1902 during the Boer War, his mother took him to Milan, Italy where the boy was educated, becoming trilingual in the process. Graduating in 1912, young West decided to study law at Genoa University, but two years later, on the outbreak of war, he made his way to England. Enlisting immediately as a private in the Royal Army Medical Corps, he was later commissioned in an Irish regiment and spent most of 1915 in the trenches.

Operational observer

Like so many future airmen, West was led by the primitive conditions of the ground war to seek another means of service and a chance flight in an aeroplane of No 3 Squadron RFC led him to volunteer for transfer to flying duties with the Royal Flying Corps. After brief training in England, West returned to France as a probationary observer in April 1916 and was posted to No 3 Squadron which was equipped with parasol-wing Morane-Saulnier machines. Flying many operational sorties over the Western Front, West became obsessed with the idea of becoming a pilot and he volunteered for every possible sortie in order to increase his total operational flying hours. By July 1917 he had accumulated more than 100 hours as an operational observer and, in October, with an overall total of 225 flying hours in his log-book, he applied for pilot training.

West was trained in England and made his first solo flight on 15 November. He totted up 60 hours as a solo pilot and was awarded his RFC 'wings' at Christmas. On 4 January 1918 he was duly posted back to France for further service, joining No 8 Squadron based near Amiens, commanded by Major Trafford Leigh-Mallory and flying the cumbersome Armstrong Whitworth FK8 two-seater. The unit's main roles were tactical co-operation with the Army, spotting for the artillery, general reconnaissance and providing aerial assistance to the relatively few tank formations then coming into use. The FK8 was a strong, functional machine, powered by a reliable 160hp Beardmore engine, which, fully-loaded, could reach a maximum speed of almost 145 km/h (90 mph). Its defensive armament was the standard pair of machine guns: a fixed Vickers for the pilot and a Scarff ring-mounted Lewis gun for the observer in the rear seat. Though decidedly inferior in general performance to its main German fighter opponents, the FK8 was well-liked by its crews and gave sterling service throughout 1918.

Ground-support duties

West settled easily into the Squadron's daily tasks and gradually gained wide experience in low-level co-operation with the ground forces. In March he flew regularly with Lieutenant John A. G. Haslam, and the two men

shared a series of hazardous sorties during the German spring offensive which commenced on 21 March 1918. One particularly dangerous sortie was on 23 April when the pair set out to bomb a concentration of enemy transport vehicles deep in German-occupied territory. Having reached their target, bombed and strafed it, West set out to recross the front lines, running the gauntlet of an intense barrage of groundfire which riddled the FK8's engine and shot an aileron away. The bomber scraped across the trenches and accomplished a safe landing a mere hundred yards inside Allied lines. The nature of the unit's low-level infantry co-operation meant repeatedly bringing home scarred and damaged machines and, on 1 May, West and Haslam were each awarded a Military Cross for their courage and determination.

Captain F. M. F. West was commissioned in the Royal Munster Fusiliers in 1914, and, after service in France, transferred to the RFC in 1917. Wounded three times in combat and mentioned twice in dispatches, West's gallantry and devotion to duty were recognised by the awards of the Victoria Cross and Military Cross. West also received the Cavaliere Crown of Italy

Groundfire was by no means the only problem for the FK8 crews; all too often they were targets for the ever-present German fighters over the fighting zones. During a bombing sortie on 18 June, with Lieutenant D. R. Sharman as observer, West was interrupted by four Pfalz scouts which dived on the FK8. West quickly shot down one Pfalz, while Sharman sent a second spinning down out of control. More Scouts joined the fray but West skilfully evaded these and flew back to base. Next day, still with Sharman, West set out for Mericourt on another bombing sortie, but was 'jumped' by a group of Fokkers before he reached his target. Dropping to an altitude of 60m (200 ft), West flew through a network of kite balloon cables before the Fokkers waiting above him were tackled by some Allied fighters, giving West an opportunity to complete his original sortie. On return to base, he was greeted with the news of his promotion to captain and flight commander.

On 1 July, No 8 Squadron RAF was officially attached to the Tank Corps for co-operation duties, as part of the preparation for the imminent Allied offensive along the Amiens front. When, on 8 August, the first waves of Allied infantry began to advance, West and his fellow FK8 pilots were compelled to fly through dense fog to cover the tank formations. Indeed, the fog was so thick that he only relocated his airfield with the aid of flares fired from the ground, and even then he crashed on landing, suffering superficial injuries. Next day West and Haslam were flying again, attacking German troops from tree-top height, when their engine was crippled by small-arms fire and West was lucky to regain the Allied lines and make a safe landing.

VC action

The morning of 10 August 1918 was misty with layers of damp fog and cloud; West and Haslam set out in an FK8 from their base at Vignacourt to liaise with a tank formation advancing towards Roye. Climbing above the low clouds, West headed south-east, seeking gaps in the clouds to locate the tanks. One clear gap over a large wood in the Ham-Hombleux area gave him a chance to verify his whereabouts and he spotted a huge concentration of German troops and vehicles around the wood. Avoiding a hail of groundfire, West climbed into cloud cover, but, still determined to assess accurately the strength of this German force, he dived through the mists again. As he did so a loose formation of German fighters attacked the FK8 from behind. One burst of machine-gun fire slashed into West's cockpit, shattering the aeroplane's wireless set

still under attack from one persistent German fighter. His shattered left leg was bleeding badly and he twisted his trouser leg into a form of tourniquet with his left hand. However, he realised that with his injuries he could never reach Vignacourt; he therefore lifted his useless left leg off the rudder bar and put the FK8 down in a shaky forced landing, still under fire from the German fighter.

West was removed from the FK8 and taken to the nearest casualty station where, before permitting the medics to operate on him, he insisted on delivering his report of the German troop concentrations. He then lapsed into unconsciousness and, when he finally recovered his senses, he found that the surgeon had amputated his left leg. On 8 November the *London Gazette* announced the award of the Victoria Cross to West, and the following month he was discharged, with a 'compensation' award of two-hundred-and-fifty pounds. The following year he met the Swiss manufacturer, Desoutter, who fashioned a new design of false leg for West. With Hugh Trenchard's influence, West was eventually granted a permanent commission in the Royal Air Force, and even took up flying again. His career between the wars was fairly routine, including service in Malta, while from 1933 until

and wounding him in the right foot.

Despite the pain West continued his dive, flew low over the massed German infantry, verifying its precise position, then turned for home in order to get this vital information to the local Allied commanders. However, he ran straight into five more German fighters which attacked immediately. West and Haslam fought bravely against superior odds before one fighter sank a full burst through West's cockpit, sending five bullets into West's left leg, smashing flesh and bone and severing an artery. The shock of the impact tore West's hand from the control column and the FK8 began to fall. Semi-conscious, West regained control just above the trees and headed westwards,

Above: on behalf of the RAF Museum, Hendon, West (left) receives Baron Manfred von Richthofen's flying helmet from the German ace's nephew in the shadow of his portrait. Above right: West (right) pictured with the AOC of No 38 Group in August 1978 at RAF Upavon, where West served with the Central Flying School in 1926

1936 he commanded No 4 Squadron at Farnborough. At the outbreak of World War II he was in command of RAF Odiham, in Hampshire.

In 1940 West was promoted to air commodore and by June 1940 was with the British Legation in Berne, Switzerland. Here he remained throughout World War II, inaugurating a successful escape route for Allied servicemen who had been interned in neutral Switzerland. Indeed, at one stage the Gestapo placed a high price on West's life because of his underground activities. His services were recognised at the end of the war by the award of a CBE. Freddie West retired from the Royal Air Force in 1946.

Westland

The Yeovil, Somerset company which followed military aircraft production with a successful range of helicopters

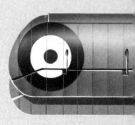

Percy Petter was one of twin brothers who, from the early 1900s, had operated a successful company in Yeovil, Somerset. Products of the firm included oil engines, lorry components and, during World War I, 18 pound shell cases. The brothers' first aeronautical involvement was the production of Short Type 184 seaplanes which the Petters were asked to build after offering their company's resources to the Board of Admiralty and the War Office.

The Petters decided to recruit someone with aircraft-building experience and Robert A. Bruce, a newly-commissioned Royal Navy lieutenant who had worked with the British and Colonial Aeroplane Co at Filton, was released by the Admiralty to become manager of the Petters' aircraft works. Another recruit to these works was Arthur Davenport, Petter's air-minded chief draughtsman who had earlier tried unsuccessfully to move to the Royal Aircraft Factory at Farnborough. The site for this new works was an area of meadowland to the west of Yeovil, which was named Westland by Percy Petter's wife.

Wartime production

It was at the Westland aircraft works that construction of 15 Type 184 seaplanes was undertaken, with the first aircraft being delivered to Shorts by January 1916. Just five months later the fourth Westland-built Type 184, powered by a Sunbeam engine, became the first spotter aircraft to be used for naval reconnaissance. Acting on orders from Admiral Sir David Beatty, at the Battle of Jutland, HMS *Engadine* sent up this aircraft, flown by Flt Lt F. J. Rutland, with Asst Paymaster G. S. Trewen as observer. They spotted and reported by wireless the position of four enemy light cruisers, thus proving the efficacy of aerial reconnaissance by naval seaplanes.

Westland ultimately built 32 Short seaplanes, all delivered by rail to Rochester for testing by Short's pilots. The first landplanes produced at Yeovil were 50 Sopwith 1½-Strutters for the Royal Flying Corps and 25 for the Royal Naval Air Service, the latter batches, built during the spring of 1917, being tested and delivered from Westland's recently-constructed aerodrome.

As the company grew in size and efficiency, the first of 150 de Havilland DH4s appeared on its factory production lines and by April 1917 were being delivered to the RFC in France. These reconnaissance-bombers, powered by 200 hp Beardmore, 250 hp Rolls-Royce Falcon or Eagle engines, were followed by 150 DH9s, fitted with 300 hp Siddeley Puma power plants.

First designs

Although Westland was primarily a production unit, an urgent Air Board requirement for the DH9A day bomber powered by the 400 hp US-built Liberty engine gave the company a chance to show its design prowess. As a result Westland became the parent company for the DH9A – known familiarly as the 'Ninak' – building 423 of the 900 completed by the war's end. More than 300 were delivered to the RAF postwar and many remained in peacetime service until 1931. It was standard equipment with 12 home-based and 11 overseas squadrons, seeing wide service both with the Auxiliary Air Force from its inception in 1925 and Flying Training Schools.

Concurrently Westland built a special erecting shop at Yeovil to house construction of 25 Vimy twin-engined bombers. Responsible for flight testing these aircraft were Sqn Ldr Rollo Haig, from the Aircraft Experimental Establishment, Martlesham Heath and Capt A. S. Kepp, an Air Ministry test pilot who later joined the company.

First design to bear the Westland name was that of

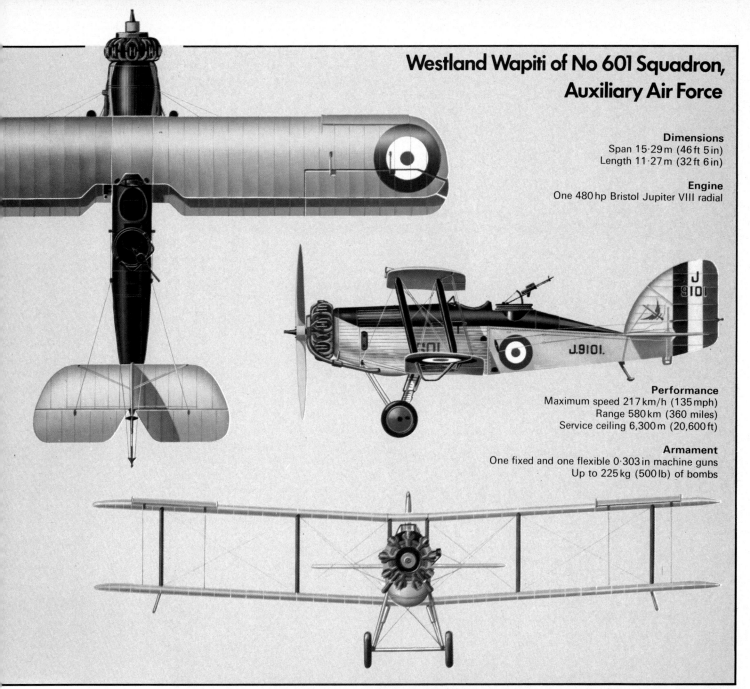

Westland Wapiti of No 601 Squadron, Auxiliary Air Force

Dimensions
Span 15·29 m (46 ft 5 in)
Length 11·27 m (32 ft 6 in)

Engine
One 480 hp Bristol Jupiter VIII radial

Performance
Maximum speed 217 km/h (135 mph)
Range 580 km (360 miles)
Service ceiling 6,300 m (20,600 ft)

Armament
One fixed and one flexible 0·303 in machine guns
Up to 225 kg (500 lb) of bombs

Right: the first original Westland design was the N.16 fighter floatplane. This aircraft did not appear until World War I had ended and only prototypes were built.
Left: Westland designed the Wapiti as a successor to the DH9A with the RAF`s overseas bomber squadrons. No 55 Squadron, whose aircraft are pictured, flew Wapitis in Iraq between 1930 and 1937

December 1918 for a compact little fighter floatplane, the N.16, which was the work of Bruce and Davenport. Powered by 150 hp Bentley rotary engines prototypes of the N.16 and an improved version, the N.17, were test flown at the Isle of Grain but did not enter production as landplane fighters proved superior in performance. The first Westland landplane was the lightweight Wagtail first flown in 1918 and intended for high-altitude fighter reconnaissance duties. Originally powered by the un-reliable 170 hp ABC Wasp, an Armstrong Lynx was later installed. Although a visually appealing aeroplane it did not advance beyond the production of five prototypes. The Weasel two-seat fighter of late 1918 was bedevilled by having the 320 hp ABC Dragonfly engine. Four prototypes served useful lives as test beds for Armstrong Siddeley and Bristol power units.

Westland's first commercial aeroplane, flown in 1919, was an attempt to introduce saloon-car comfort to flying. Of wood and fabric construction, the limousine two-bay biplane was fitted with a 275 hp Rolls-Royce Falcon III engine. The three-passenger cabin was plywood-covered and housed the pilot, whose seat was raised 0·76 m (30 in) to allow his head to protrude through an open hatch. One Limousine I and six Limousine IIs were produced, several flying with Instone Air Lines and Sidney Cotton's Aerial Survey Co in Newfoundland. The first of two Limousine IIIs, with 450 hp Napier Lion engines, won first prize in the small aeroplane class of the 1920 Air Ministry Commercial Aeroplane Competition. This 196 km/h (118 mph) variant had a nose-wheel added to prevent the aircraft nosing over when the wheel-brakes were applied, and had a spacious five-passenger cabin.

In parallel with this limited Limousine production the Westland design office created the Walrus, an inelegant redesign of the DH9A to meet an Air Ministry requirement for a fleet spotter. With a crew of three the Walrus had unstaggered 14 m (46 ft) span folding wings, arrestor gear

and emergency flotation gear, with armament of one fixed Vickers gun and a Lewis gun on a Scarff ring. It needed all of the Lion's 450 hp to give a 181 km/h (115 mph) top speed, but nevertheless 36 Walrus aircraft were produced between 1920 and 1924.

The Lion-powered Dreadnought Postal Monoplane, built during 1923, was of very advanced appearance and embodied the design ideas of a Russian, M. Voyevodsky. The 21 m (70 ft) span wing had five tubular metal spars, wooden ribs and fabric covering; the fuselage was of wood. The Dreadnought first flew on 9 May 1923 with West-land's pilot Capt Keep at the controls, but soon after take-off it stalled and crashed, seriously injuring the pilot.

DH9A derivatives

During the early 1920s Westland struggled hard to keep going and existed, like several other British aircraft companies, by designing and building a range of aero-planes utilising DH9A major assemblies. Westland's factory also undertook the reconditioning and modification of 'Ninaks', while its design office was busy with an entry for the 1924 Light Aeroplane Trials at Lympne. The tiny Woodpigeon and the almost equally small Widgeon monoplane were Westland's entries, the former being a wood-and-fabric two-seater powered by a 32 hp Bristol Cherub III and the latter a parasol monoplane of similar construction with a 35 hp Blackburne Thrush engine. Only two Woodpidgeons were built, but 30 Widgeons I, II and III were produced during 1927–28 with various engines.

Several companies responded to the Air Ministry's issue of Specification 26/23, calling for a two-seat long-range day bomber with a 650 hp Rolls-Royce Condor III engine. From Westland came Arthur Davenport's Yeovil,

Below: the Westland-Hill Pterodactyl tailless sesquiplane fighter was a private venture designed by Capt G. T. R. Hill in 1924. The Mark IB is illustrated.
Opposite: Westland's interest in autogiros resulted in the unsuccessful C.29 of 1934 and the CL.20 (illustrated), which first flew on 14 February 1935

the first of three mixed construction wood and metal prototypes being flown from Andover during June 1925 by Capt Courtney. Although the 18 m (59 ft 6 in) span Yeovil was a heavy aircraft weighing nearly four tons, it could carry the specified 236 kg (520 lb) bomb-load at the required 193 km/h (120 mph). However, Hawker's Horsley was judged the winner and entered production, with the Yeovil prototypes relegated to flight development of propellers and other equipment.

Westland were equally unsuccessful in the Air Ministry's Specification 4/24 competition for a twin-engined fighter armed with two heavy calibre cannon. Arthur Davenport's Westbury, powered by two 450 hp Bristol Jupiter VIs and carrying a pair of 37 mm Coventry Ordnance Works (COW) guns, provided useful experience in solving structural and armament installation and firing problems, but no orders resulted. While the second Westbury was being built, hopes of a production order were revived with the Wizard single-seat fighter, built as a private venture during 1926. This parasol monoplane, which diverged sharply from standard British design practice, was initially powered by a 490 hp Falcon III, but ultimately had a top speed of 232 km/h (188 mph) with a supercharged Rolls-Royce 'F' engine. However, the later use of a 480 hp Kestrel II proved its downfall and it, too, failed to win a production contract.

Gloster, Handley Page and Hawker all produced biplanes to meet Specification 23/25 for a two-seat, single-

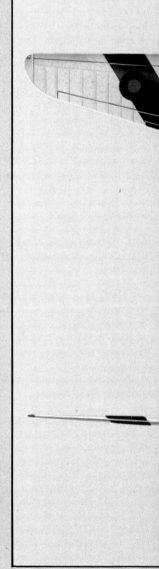

engined high-altitude bomber; Westland tendered an 18 m (61 ft) span parasol monoplane design. Designed originally around the 495 hp Bristol Orion – which failed to materialise – the Witch first flew with a 420 hp Jupiter VI engine in 1928. No production resulted, however, and the prototype ended its days at Henlow's Parachute Training Unit.

The Wapiti

In 1927 the Air Ministry issued Specification 26/27 to produce a new two-seat general purpose aircraft to replace a number of ageing and outmoded types, including the DH9A. Increased performance and better load-carrying ability were paramount requirements but, for reasons of economy, the new design was required to use as many DH9A components as possible. Orders for military aircraft were few and far between and the re-

quirement brought proposals from seven companies. Westland, which had developed the 'Ninak', was in a strong position to meet the need for a successor; Davenport submitted the Wapiti, which used the wings, tail unit, ailerons and interplane struts of the DH9A.

With a deeper, wider fuselage than its predecessor, the prototype Wapiti was of mixed wood and metal construction with a direct-drive 420 hp Jupiter VI engine. Armament was a fixed forward-firing Vickers gun and a Scarff-ring-mounted Lewis gun for the observer. The 263 kg (580 lb) bomb-load was carried on underwing and fuselage racks.

Major L. P. Openshaw made the first flight early in 1927 and it was soon discovered that the DH9A rudder was ineffective and a larger unit was fitted. After lengthy trials at Martlesham Heath, the Wapiti Mark I was ordered into production – the first Westland military design to

reach this stage–in December 1927, with the first batch of 25 aircraft being built during 1928. In that year No 84 Squadron RAF, based at Shaibah, Iraq, was the first to receive the Wapiti.

The Wapiti Mark IB, with a divided landing gear and a Jupiter, VIIIF was sold to South Africa, while the Wapiti Mark II was an all-metal variant. In 1931 came the Mark IIA, followed by a single Wapiti Mark IV with a Jaguar VI engine and finally a Mark VI two-seat trainer. Other variants featured a range of engines; some had floats and undercarriages, some were equipped for long-range desert operations, while one aircraft was reserved for the personal use of HRH the Prince of Wales. These various sub-types brought the production total to 565 Wapitis. Between 12 December 1928 and 25 February 1929, Wapitis of No 20 Squadron escorted No 70 Squadron's Vickers Victoria troop-carriers through the Khyber Pass to Peshawar as they evacuated 586 people from Kabul, the Afghan capital, during the disturbances there. In January 1933 four Wapitis of No 28 Squadron flew 9,800 km (6,200 miles) from Ambala in the Punjab, to Singapore

Wapitis also served with nine Auxiliary Air Force squadrons from October 1929 when No 600 Squadron at Hendon received its aircraft. Although retired in 1937, about 80 Wapitis were still with the RAF in India in 1939. Overseas customers for Wapitis were the Royal Canadian

Air Force, Royal Australian Air Force, South African Air Force and the Chinese Central Government.

Tailless fighter

Development of the range of tailless Pterodactyl aircraft began in 1924 with the first flight of the Mark I glider designed by Capt G. T. R. Hill. His aim was an aircraft which could not get out of control through an error on the part of the pilot, and Westland entered enthusiastically into the building of these unique aeroplanes. Three Pterodactyls were built, each in turn having more powerful engines, culminating in 1932 in the two-seat Pterodactyl Mark V sesquiplane fighter with a tractor-mounted steam-cooled 600 hp Rolls-Royce Goshawk engine. The parasol main wing was swept back nearly 45 degrees and carried a fin and rudder at each tip. A tandem two-wheel landing gear was fitted in the main nacelle with small outrigger wheels. Armament was two forward-firing 0·303 in Vickers guns for the pilot and two Lewis guns in an electrically-operated turret for the gunner behind him, who enjoyed an almost totally unrestricted field of fire to the rear and side. The aircraft flew well, with a top speed of 180 km/h (113 mph) and an absolute ceiling of 5,180 m (17,000 ft), but this private-venture development was not ordered.

Arthur Davenport designed the Interceptor low-wing

Far left: the Lysander entered RAF service in 1938 as an army co-operation machine and it operated in this role during the Battle of France and in the Western Desert. Other duties that it undertook included agent dropping, air/sea rescue and target towing.
Below left: the RAF Museum's Lysander is preserved in the markings of No 225 Squadron

Westland Lysander TT Mark III of the RCAF

Dimensions
Span 15·24 m (50 ft)
Length 10·66 m (30 ft 6 in)
Height 4·87 m (11 ft 6 in)

Engine
One 870 hp Bristol Mercury XXX

Performance
Maximum speed 335 km/h (209 mph)
Service ceiling 6,550 m (21,500 ft)

Weights
Empty 1,979 kg (4,365 lb)
Loaded 2,864 kg (6,318 lb)

Top: the Welkin pressurised interceptor was designed against the possibility of German high-altitude bombing raids, but the type did not enter front-line service. The prototype, which first flew on 1 November 1942, is illustrated here.
Centre: the prototype Whirlwind first flew at Boscombe Down on 11 October 1938 and a contract for 200 was placed in January 1939.
Above: a prototype Wyvern with a Rolls-Royce Eagle piston engine is preserved at the Fleet Air Arm Museum

company name in the headlines. The first was the PV.3, a carrier-borne torpedo-bomber, built in 1931 as a private venture. The second was a cleaned-up private venture Wapiti development known as the Wapiti VII or PV.6, with a 520hp Pegasus engine. It featured a longer fuselage, spatted landing gear, a tailwheel and wheel-brakes, and in 1932 twelve Wapitis converted to this standard and named Wallace Mark I, were ordered.

A further 56 similarly-converted Wapitis were ordered for general purpose and light bomber duties, before the Wallace II to Specification G31/35 was produced. It embodied enclosed cockpits for the two crew, which also provided protection for the gunner when the 'lobster-back' section of the canopy was opened, and a 680hp Pegasus IV giving a 254km/h (158mph) top speed. Wallace production totalled 172, the majority going to the Auxiliary Air Force or the Anti-Aircraft Co-operation Flight at Biggin Hill for target-towing duties. When World War II began, 83 Wallaces were on RAF strength.

First over Everest

The remodelled PV.3 and a modified Wallace were employed by the Houston Mount Everest Expedition of 1932/33. The objective was the first flight over this mountain's peak and the aircraft were required to have an operating ceiling of at least 10,000m (33,000ft). On test Harald Penrose flew the PV.3 from Yeovil to a height of 11,400m (37,500ft). Both aircraft were powered by specially-prepared 525hp Pegasus IS3 engines and were modified to have an enclosed rear cabin for an observer/photographer plus heating and oxygen systems. Sadly, both aircraft used by the successful Expedition were broken up several years later.

No fewer than nine companies submitted entries to meet Specification G4/31 for an all-purpose aircraft for day and night bombing, army co-operation, dive-bombing, reconnaissance, photography, casualty evacuation and torpedo-bombing duties. All were biplanes except for Westland's PV.7 high-wing monoplane, visually owing much to the Wallace, which was fitted with a 722hp

monoplane around a 440hp Bristol Mercury IIA engine to meet Specification F20/27 for a single-seat high-altitude fighter. The prototype first flew during 1929 but was not able to win a production contract. Westland's design thoughts continued to range over both civil and military types, and two in the former category, the Westland IV and the Wessex achieved some success during 1929–37. A small three-engined high-wing six-seat taxi aircraft, the prototype Westland IV had 95hp ADC Cirrus III engines; the second aircraft, powered by 105hp Cirrus Hermes, was sold to Imperial Airways and was scrapped only in 1940. Ten examples of the Wessex, powered by Armstrong Siddeley Genet Major engines, were built, four being operated by Sabena, the Belgian airline on its European routes.

During the late 1920s the Air Ministry still had hopes of using the 37mm shell-firing COW gun in aircraft and specified its use in designs to meet Specification F29/27 for a single-seat fighter. Westland produced in 1931 a modified version of the earlier Interceptor with a 485hp Mercury IIIA driving a four-bladed propeller. The single COW gun, mounted on the cockpit sides pointed upwards at an angle of 55 degrees, was intended to fire high-explosive shells into bomber formations above it, but the whole project was cancelled.

Although Westland had produced a number of monoplanes, it was two biplanes which ultimately put the

Pegasus IIM3 radial engine with a Townend ring cowling, to give a 278 km/h (173 mph) top speed. However, all hopes of its adoption for RAF service ended in the late summer of 1934 when the prototype crashed at Martlesham Heath after the port rear main bracing strut failed and the wing came off.

Following lengthy delays with the development programme on the steam-cooled Goshawk engine, the trials of contenders for contracts to Specification F7/30, calling for a single-seat four-gun day interceptor and night fighter, were postponed until 1935. Seven companies built prototypes of which Arthur Davenport's PV.4 was the most unorthodox, featuring a mid-fuselage-mounted 600 hp Goshawk IIS driving a two-blade propeller through a long shaft. The pilot sat high up in an enclosed cabin in front of the upper wing, with four Vickers guns mounted in the fuselage sides ahead of the engine. Built in 1934 of metal with fabric covering, it had sharply-staggered single-bay wings and a divided and spatted main landing gear. Unfortunately for Westland, the PV.4's performance was considerably below that of other F7/30 aspirants and trials were abandoned in 1935.

Westland also built the C.29 autogiro in 1934, with Juan de la Cierva, the pioneer of rotating-wing aircraft, co-operating in the design. A five-seat machine powered by an Armstrong Siddeley Panther radial engine driving a two-blade metal propeller, the C.29 was of very advanced design. Severe ground resonance was discovered during ground testing and the C.29 never flew. The CL.20 side-by-side two-seat cabin autogiro was built by Westland to the design of George Lepere and first flew on 14th February 1935. Although it flew successfully and handled quite well, further development was abandoned.

Yet another prototype built at Yeovil by Westland during 1934 was the Hendy Heck single-engined low-wing monoplane designed by Basil Henderson to meet an order by Whitney Straight for a small high-performance three-seat aeroplane. The year also saw the retirement of R. A. Bruce and the appointment of W. E. W. 'Teddy' Petter as technical director of the company.

The Lizzie at war
A major milestone in the company's history was passed in July 1935 when Westland Aircraft Works became a public company and was renamed Westland Aircraft Ltd. Westland—and certainly Teddy Petter—had a marked inclination toward aeroplanes of unusual appearance, and their contender to meet the A39/34 Specification for an army co-operation aircraft was yet another unmistakable design. It was essential for the pilot and observer to have an unobstructed view of the ground and this led Petter to create an all-metal fabric-covered high-wing strut-braced monoplane design named the Lysander. A landing gear retracting into a stub wing was initially proposed, but the heavily-spatted cantilever main struts—made possible by the use of Dowty internally-sprung wheels—which were finally adopted were lighter and created no more drag. Moreover, they housed two fixed Browning guns, landing lights and carried small stub wings to provide attachment points for supply containers or six anti-personnel bombs. The observer was armed with a Vickers gun on a swivel mounting in the rear cockpit. Both the pilot and observer had enclosed accommodation with provision for the rear canopy to be opened for gun firing.

The 15m (50ft) span wing, a mixture of compound tapers and varying in thickness, was fully slotted and flapped to permit take-offs and landings to be made at slow speeds and at alarming angles. The all-silver Lysander

Above: the Whirlwind, a development of the Sikorsky S-55, served with RAF Transport and Coastal Commands. The turboshaft Whirlwind HAR Mark 10 (illustrated) replaced the piston-engined HAR Mark 2 from 1960. Left: the Widgeon was a modified Dragonfly produced in small numbers. The Dragonfly, based on the Sikorsky S-51, was Westland's first helicopter and served with civil operators, the RAF and the Royal Navy

prototype first flew on 15 June 1936, piloted by Harald Penrose. It was powered by an 890hp Bristol Mercury XII radial engine which gave a maximum speed of 370km/h (229mph), and the type's stalling speed was only 88km/h 55mph. With a full load the Lysander could clear a 15m (50ft) high obstacle in 210 metres (230 yards), the ground run being only 150m (165 yards).

A contract for the first 144 Lysander Mark Is was placed in September 1936 and the type entered RAF service with No 16 Squadron, based at Old Sarum, Wiltshire, in June 1938. This Squadron had had a long association with the Army, beginning in 1915, and continued with this ground support role in France in September 1939 as part of the Air Component of the British Expeditionary Force. Other Lysander-equipped units which moved to France were Nos 2, 4, 13 and 26 Squadrons. Their task was primarily artillery spotting and reconnaissance, but one Lysander took a more militant role in November 1939 and shot down the first Heinkel He 111 bomber to be destroyed over BEF territory.

Through the harsh winter conditions of 1939–40 the 'Lizzie' or the 'Flying Carrot' as the Lysander became known to the RAF, performed good service as the eyes of the Army. During the black days of May and June 1940, when the evacuation of the BEF from Dunkirk was under way, the Lysanders were used to drop supplies to Allied troops defending an ever-shrinking perimeter around Calais, while others flew in the ground-attack role against enemy positions. Lysanders of No 4 Squadron were the last aircraft of the Air Component to be in action before flying back to England. During the Battle of France some 50 Lysanders were shot down and over 30 were destroyed on the ground.

Twelve Lysanders came under Fighter Command control during August 1940 for air-sea rescue duties and were the first aircraft used for this specialised task. They were later joined by Supermarine Walrus amphibians to form a chain of units from Valley, Anglesey around the south and east coastline to Coltishall, Norfolk. For three years the ungainly Lysanders continued the air-sea rescue service, earning the nickname 'The Salvation Navy'.

Clandestine flights

In the Western Desert campaigns, Lysanders of Nos 6 and 208 Squadrons RAF and, later, No 3 Squadron Royal Australian Air Force, were engaged in a hotly-contested air war from early 1940 until they were replaced by Hawker Hurricane fighters in May 1941. Operating from desert strips close to the troops for whom they flew, the Lysander crews performed photo-reconnaissance, ground-attack, rescue and supply-dropping duties in the face of fierce opposition from the Luftwaffe and Regia Aeronautica. In India too, where Nos 1, 2, 3 and 4 Squadrons Indian Air Force flew their Lysanders alongside No 28 Squadron RAF, the aeroplane performed invaluable reconnaissance work over difficult jungle terrain during the Japanese advance of 1940–42.

A unique role for the Lysander was the clandestine dropping and collection of special agents–known as 'Joes'–in occupied Europe. One of the main airfields for these hazardous operations was Tempsford, Bedfordshire, but flights were also made from other airfields, including Tangmere, Sussex. Fitted with a long-range fuel tank and a mounting ladder to the rear cockpit, the all-black Lysanders of No 138 Squadron, in the hands of brave pilots, needed only an isolated level field and a moonlit night to perform this highly-dangerous but essential task. The first drop and pick-up was in 1941, and

this work for the Special Operations Executive reached its peak in 1943 when 60 agents were ferried into Europe and 81 were brought back to England. Special Duties Lysanders also operated in this role in the Mediterranean and South-East Asia theatres of operations.

Four-cannon fighter

In 1936 as engine powers increased and fighters became faster, so their armament was developed to become heavier to compensate for the reduced time a target aircraft was in the sights of an attacking pilot. This was particularly apparent in Europe where the Swiss Oerlikon 20mm cannon was proving very successful. Specification F37/35 called for a single-seat day and night fighter with four such cannon, and of four projects submitted by Bristol, Hawker, Supermarine and Westland it was the latter company's P.9 Whirlwind which was chosen for prototype production. Designed by Petter, the all-metal Whirlwind was another unmistakable aeroplane, with a long slim fuselage, the nose housing four 20mm Hispano cannon, a 14m (45ft) span high-aspect-ratio wing carrying two 885hp Rolls-Royce Peregrine inline engines in slim nacelles and with the tailplane set high on the fin. Its top speed was 580km/h (360mph) at 4,570m (15,000ft).

The prototype Whirlwind was first flown on 11 October 1938 piloted by Harald Penrose. Although the Peregrine engines gave endless trouble during the development trials–as they did throughout their service life–these were completed successfully. During 1938 John Brown and Co., the Clydeside shipbuilding firm, acquired from Petters Ltd a controlling interest in Westland Aircraft. The remainder of Petters' holding was taken over sometime later by AEI.

The Whirlwind was ordered into production in January 1939 and was the first Westland fighter to reach this status. First deliveries to No 263 Squadron at Exeter were made in June 1940. The Squadron became operational with the Whirlwind in the following December and claimed its first kill, an Arado Ar 196 floatplane, in February 1941, having recorded a probable victory over a Junkers Ju 88 in the previous month.

There were some continuing engine problems; maintenance was not easy as the Peregrine was only used in the Whirlwind, and pilots found that aircraft performance deteriorated with increasing altitude. However, the aircraft was fast at low altitudes, the four cannon armament provided concentrated fire-power and the range was greater than other contemporary fighters. For these reasons the Whirlwind frequently flew on 'Rhubarbs', low-level operations against enemy airfields, tanks, shipping and ground installations. No 137 Squadron was formed in September 1941 with Whirlwinds and added weight to the long-range convoy escort and night intruder activities of No 263 Squadron.

Whirlwinds gave way to Hawker Typhoons in these squadrons late in 1943, but just a year earlier, on 1 November 1942, Harald Penrose had taken the prototype of the Whirlwind's successor, the Welkin, into the air for the first time. A very high altitude single-seat fighter built to meet Specification F7/41, the Welkin was powered by two 1,650hp two-stage supercharged Rolls-Royce Merlin engines. The dominant design features were a very high aspect ratio 21m (70ft) span wing–the largest ever on a single-seat fighter–and a self-contained light-alloy pressure cabin with armoured steel bulkheads fore and aft, the whole unit being attached to the wing's main spar. At Boscombe Down the Welkin was heavily criticised for, although it had a maximum speed of 622km/h (387mph)

Left: first ordered for the Royal Air Force in August 1961, the Wessex was a turbine-engined derivative of the Sikorsky S-58. The type had earlier entered service with the Fleet Air Arm, with which it was to perform in the assault and anti-submarine warfare roles.
Inset left: the Scout has been a mainstay of the Army Air Corps since the early 1960s. Air-to-surface missiles mounted on pylons have increased the type's fire-power.
Inset right: examples of the Wessex were flown by civil operators on oilfield support and other duties. A Wessex 60 of Bristow Helicopters is illustrated

and make these specialised products. It was considered that helicopters, with their unique capabilities, would be a major growth sector of aviation, and in 1947 Westland acquired from the Sikorsky company the manufacturing rights of the S-51 four-seat helicopter then being produced in the United States.

While helicopter development plans progressed at Yeovil, the fixed-wing interests continued with the design, by John Digby, of the Wyvern, a Rolls-Royce Eagle-engined naval strike fighter to Specification N11/44. First flown on 16 December 1946, the aircraft soon encountered problems with the big 3,550 hp Eagle engine and its two 4m (13ft) diameter contra-rotating propellers. Several prototypes were built before interest turned to the use of propeller-turbines in this aircraft. As a result trials were flown with a Wyvern powered by a Rolls-Royce Clyde engine. In the event, the Wyvern TF Mark 2 torpedo fighter entered production with an Armstrong Siddeley Python turboprop, even though Westland's pilots preferred the lower-powered Clyde.

Westland and the engine manufacturer were pioneering in a new field of propulsion, however. Wyvern development was lengthy, but in May 1953 this big aeroplane joined the Fleet with No 813 Squadron based at Ford, Sussex. It was not until September 1954 that the unit embarked its Wyverns on HMS *Albion*. No 827 Squadron was the second unit to get afloat with Wyverns in HMS *Eagle*,

Top: Westland's diminutive Wasp was designed primarily for operation from small platforms on frigates and destroyers in the anti-submarine warfare role. A Wasp of No 829 Squadron Fleet Air Arm, attached to HMS Rothesay, is pictured. Above: originally a Bristol type, the Belvedere was inherited by Westland in 1960. The first twin-engined twin-rotor helicopter to enter service with the Royal Air Force, the Belvedere could carry 18 fully-armed troops

at 7,920 m (26,000 ft) and could fly at heights of more than 12,190 km/h (40,000 ft), the handling characteristics were so poor that a full roll took nearly 15 seconds to complete and it could be easily outmanoeuvred by a de Havilland Mosquito. Despite this severe limitation, 67 production Welkins were built, plus one example of a two-seat Welkin Mark II night fighter. However, enemy high-altitude attacks never materialised in the strengths envisaged and the Welkin never entered RAF squadron service, being used mainly for research at very great heights.

Throughout a large part of the war Westland was also involved with the production of Spitfires and Seafires, building 2,094 examples and a handful of Fairey Barracudas. Major components were also fabricated for the Armstrong Whitworth Albemarle and the US-built Curtiss Tomahawk and Kittyhawk fighters.

An immediate postwar development was high-altitude pressurisation and breathing equipment with a subsidiary company, Normalair Ltd, being formed in 1946 to design

some eight months later, but after overseas service the aircraft went to Nos 830 and 831 Squadrons.

No 830 Squadron was the sole Wyvern-equipped unit to see action. Flying from HMS *Eagle*, the Squadron flew in the Suez Campaign, making the first of 18 attacks on 1 November 1956. The Squadron flew 79 sorties, losing two aircraft but with both pilots being rescued. A total of 127 Wyverns was built to serve until March 1958 with eight Fleet Air Arm squadrons and several other Conversion and Development Units. Those surviving were sold as scrap during 1958–59.

So ended Westland's long line of fixed-wing aircraft built at Yeovil. Some ten years earlier, however, the company was laying plans for a new generation of rotating-wing aircraft to supplant it. In January 1947 Westland signed an agreement with the Sikorsky Division of United Aircraft Corporation in the United States and obtained rights to produce an Anglicised version of the S-51 four-seat helicopter. By 1950 an improved variant powered by a 550 hp Alvis Leonides engine and known as the Westland-Sikorsky WS-51 Dragonfly, was in production for the RAF, Royal Navy and some overseas customers, with a total of 139 being delivered.

In the same year work began on a British version of the S-55. The Westland-Sikorsky name was dropped and when the first Yeovil-built aircraft flew on 27 March 1954, it bore the name Westland Whirlwind. Series I Whirlwinds were powered by 600 hp Pratt & Whitney Wasp or Wright Cyclone power plants, but the Series 2 aircraft had Alvis Leonides engines. One Whirlwind, mounted on floats, was used by British European Airways for a service over the 27 kilometer (17 mile) route between London Airport and a site on the south bank of the River Thames, which began in July 1955. This service closed down in 1957, however, when the south bank site was lost.

There was limited success with an improved Dragonfly, known as the Widgeon, which was modified to provide more cabin space, but development was limited. The agreement with Sikorsky was extended in February 1956 to allow licence-production of the S-58 – with the name Wessex and powered by the 1,300 hp Napier Gazelle turbine – for anti-submarine and transport duties. The first flight of an anti-submarine Wessex took place on 17 May 1957.

Turbine helicopters
After six years in production the Whirlwind had a new lease of life with the installation of a de Havilland Gnome free turbine mounted horizontally in the nose. The first Whirlwind thus powered flew on 28 February 1959, and in April 1960 Westland received a large order from the RAF for this variant, designated HAR Mark 10, and for the conversion of most piston-engined Whirlwinds then in service to turbine power.

Much more ambitious was the 14 ton Westminster, Westland's first real move into helicopter design, which flew on 15 June 1958. Although it used Sikorsky rotating components, the rest of this big machine was new and was powered by two Napier Eland turbines. Sadly there was little Government support for the Westminster and the programme was terminated.

Under Government pressure a major programme of helicopter industry rationalisation saw Westland acquire the helicopter interests of Saunders-Roe (which had earlier taken over the Cierva Autogyro Co) in July 1959. The rotary-wing departments of Bristol Aircraft and the Fairey Co were subsequently acquired during January–May 1960. Thus, virtually all responsibility for British helicopter manufacture passed to Westland, which inherited Belvedere production from Bristol, the P531 from Saunders-Roe and the Rotodyne from Fairey. Yeovil became the headquarters for the whole group with the newly-acquired companies becoming divisions at Hayes, Cowes and Weston-super-Mare.

Wessex development went ahead with the replacement of the single Gazelle with two Gnome shaft turbines; the aircraft has since been built in very large numbers and in several variants for the RAF, Royal Navy and for export. Wessex have served with the RN since 1961 for anti-submarine search and strike operations and as Commando carriers and with the RAF since 1964 as troop and freight transports.

Anglo-French collaboration
Although the Scout and Wasp stem from the P531 utility helicopter and bear an obvious relationship, they differed greatly in design and equipment. The first Scout with a 1,050 shp Nimbus engine, developed for the Royal Navy had a folding tail and rotor and a wheeled landing gear. The Scout variant with a skid landing gear was soon adopted by the British Army for reconnaissance and liaison duties. Both were widely used by British forces and those of other countries.

Production of the Belvedere totalled 26, the first RAF unit to be equipped, on 15 September 1961, being No 66

Below: accepted by the Fleet Air Arm in mid-1969, the Westland Sea King was developed from Sikorsky's SH-3D. Powered by Rolls-Royce Gnome turboshafts in place of the General Electric T58 units of the American helicopter, the Sea King also serves the Royal Air Force in the search and rescue role. A specialised tactical transport version named Commando has also been developed at Yeovil, 15 modified examples of which were ordered by the Royal Navy in mid-1978 as the Sea King HU Mark 4

Far left: two of the 30 Aérospatiale/Westland Gazelle helicopters ordered by the Fleet Air Arm for training purposes, primarily by No 705 Squadron at RNAS Culdrose, Cornwall. Left: the Puma is the second type to be covered by an Anglo-French production agreement concluded in 1968. A total of 40 Pumas entered service with the RAF from 1971. Right: formerly known as the WG.13, the Lynx completed the Aérospatiale connection and was the sole type for which Westland had design leadership. An Army Air Corps Lynx is pictured with a variety of external stores

Squadron at Odiham, Hampshire. With the power of two 1,300 shp Gazelles the Belvedere could lift 18 troops or loads of up to 2,720 kg (6,000 lb). No 26 Squadron's Belvederes lifted Marine Commandos from HMS *Centaur* into Tanganyika during the 1963 rebellion, supported the Army in the Radfan operations in South Arabia and operated throughout the Brunei Campaign of 1962–66.

A sad event was the cancellation of the Fairey Rotodyne programme in February 1962 through the lack of further Government funding and the withdrawal of orders previously placed by US and Canadian helicopter operators. So passed the opportunity for Britain and Westland to produce the most advanced rotating wing aircraft in the world.

In June 1966 Westland confirmed that it would undertake licence-production of the Sikorsky SH-3 anti-submarine helicopter and made plans to receive four US-built airframes, to be fitted with two Gnome turbines and other British equipment, for development flying. Orders for the Sea King, as it was known, built up steadily and although the RAF uses this aircraft only in the search and rescue role, the Royal Navy employs them for the anti-submarine, Commando support and transport tasks.

As part of a general round of Anglo-French discussions concerning collaborative production of Concorde, Jaguar the Airbus and the AFVG variable-geometry fighter, preliminary talks between Sud Aviation (now Aérospatiale) and Westland on future helicopter projects began on 9 November 1966. Just a month later Westland Aircraft began conducting its helicopter business through a new wholly-owned subsidiary named Westland Helicopters Ltd.

The outcome of these and further negotiations was an Anglo-French agreement on joint production of three helicopters; the Lynx, for which Westland had design leadership, and the Puma and Gazelle with Aérospatiale design control. These aircraft have since been produced

---

The WG.34 anti-submarine warfare helicopter intended to replace the FAA's Sea King in the late 1980s, is designed to operate independently of its parent ship. Such autonomy requires a wide range of complex equipment and systems. It will employ sonobuoys, rather than dipping sonar, and radar, radar intercept and towed magnetic anomaly (MAD), sensors, and the tactical information from these will be processed by a computer. The WG.34 will have a cleaner airframe than the Sea King, and three, rather than two engines, increasing payload, performance and safety.

---

in substantial quantities for the British and French forces and for export. With the Sea King the Lynx will be the principal rotating-wing aircraft used by the Royal Navy from 1980 onwards, while the Gazelle and Puma will serve RAF and Army Air Corps units in the transport, reconnaissance and training roles.

Westland developed a special tactical transport version of the Sea King named Commando and anticipates building and selling these two variants into the 1990s. The company has also projected a Sea King replacement designated WG34, which, though smaller, will carry a substantially heavier load with a higher performance. It is likely that this helicopter will be produced as a collaborative venture with other European helicopter industries.

Two Westland helicopters with a difference are the Wisp and Wideye remotely piloted craft which are part of the Supervisor battlefield surveillance system developed jointly by Westland and Marconi Avionics. In addition to its helicopter interests, Westland Aircraft has a controlling interest in British Hovercraft Corporation, and has Normalair-Garrett Ltd, FPT Ltd and Westland Engineers Ltd as subsidiary companies.

Engines
Two 1,435 shp
Turboméca Turmo IVC
turbines

Performance
Maximum speed
310 km/h (170 mph)
Range 644 km
(400 miles)
Service ceiling 6,100 m
(20,000 ft)

Westland-Aérospatiale Puma HC Mark 1

Dimensions
Rotor diameter 15 m (49 ft 2½ in)
Length 18·15 m (59 ft 6½ in)
Height 5·14 m (16 ft 10½ in)

Aerial Entrepreneur

Claude Grahame-White was one of the first Britons to exploit aviation commercially

The great Reims aviation meeting of 1909 inspired many a spectator, but none more so than a 30-year-old English motor dealer named Claude Grahame-White, who immediately enrolled at Louis Blériot's flying school at Issy-les-Moulineaux near Paris. He also ordered a 60 hp Blériot Monoplane which he named *White Eagle*. Early one November morning, however, in the absence of his instructor, Grahame-White and a friend made an unauthorised and alarming hop across Issy. Both Grahame-White and the aeroplane were promptly banished to Blériot's airfield at Pau, where the great maestro himself wrecked *White Eagle* and had to recompense the Englishman with two of his cross-Channel type monoplanes.

London to Manchester

A month later, on 16 December 1909, Grahame-White obtained his pilot's brevet from the Aéro Club de France and opened his own flying school at Pau, becoming the first British aviation school, albeit abroad. It was at Pau that he heard of the prize first offered in 1906 by Lord Northcliffe and the *Daily Mail* of ten thousand pounds to the first pilot to fly from London to Manchester within 24 hours. Many aviators had announced their intention to try for it, but all had cried off.

However, Grahame-White believed the Manchester trip could be done, but not in either of his Blériots. He approached Henri Farman at his Reims works for one of his biplanes and was not in the least discouraged when Farman suggested that he had insufficient experience for such a flight. A Farman biplane was readied and shipped to London, where Grahame-White sent in his entry for the competition on 20 April 1910. He planned to fly from Wormwood Scrubs, but London County Council forbade him to use their land, and arrangements were made instead to depart from a farm at Park Royal, flying into London first to comply with the requirement that all contestants start within an eight-kilometre (five mile) radius of Fleet Street. At 0512 hours on Saturday, 23 April 1910 Grahame-White took off and headed for the gasometer at Kensal Rise which marked the official starting point of the 298 km (185 mile) flight from London to Manchester.

Above and above right: Grahame-White pictured with his Farman at Brooklands on 26 May 1910, a month after his attempt to make the first flight between London and Manchester, in which he was beaten by Paulhan.
Top: Grahame-White pictured in his Blériot monoplane, the type on which he learned to fly in France in 1909.
Right: Grahame-White (fifth from right) during a visit to the US Navy and War Departments in late 1910. He was in the United States to compete in air races

Forced landing

After rounding the starting flag, Grahame-White set course for Willesden Junction, from where he planned to follow railway lines to Manchester. He flew at a height of barely 46m (150ft) at 64km/h (40mph), and was soon numb with cold in the chill morning air. A flask of brandy warmed both body and flagging spirits, and two hours after take-off the Farman landed at the pre-arranged stopping point at Rugby. Grahame-White's mechanics were already there, having travelled faster by motor car.

An hour later he set off again, to a blast from the whistles of railway engines as he followed their tracks to Nuneaton, Tamworth and into the Trent Valley towards Lichfield. Here, valve trouble with the biplane's Gnome engine forced him down, damaging a landing skid in the process. Worse was to come, however. While repairs were effected, a sudden gust of wind upended the Farman, inflicting damage which made further flying impossible. As Grahame-White surveyed the aircraft came news that two other entries for the race had been received by the *Daily Mail*. The Farman was rapidly dismantled, loaded aboard a special railway wagon and rushed back to London for repair ready to battle for the elusive prize with the new contestants–Emile Dubonnet and Louis Paulhan, both of them Frenchmen.

Duel with Paulhan

On arrival in London, Grahame-White and Paulhan exchanged mutual good wishes for the coming duel. Permission was obtained to use Wormwood Scrubs for the second attempt, and on the morning of Wednesday, 27 April 1910 as many as a quarter of a million spectators journeyed both there, and also to Hendon where Paulhan had set up camp, to see the start. It was raining, a cold, blustery wind seemed certain to prevent any flying and Grahame-White returned to sleep at his hotel. However, by 1600 hours the weather had improved. Paulhan elected to take off, and sent word to his rival, but the message was never delivered.

By the time that Grahame-White was eventually woken with the news, Paulhan was well on his way across London. Friends reasoned with Grahame-White that the wind was still too strong, but he insisted on going. Seventy-one minutes after Paulhan had taken off from Hendon Grahame-White was away, flying off into the dusk pursued by a fleet of cars driven by the best racing drivers of the day.

By the time he reached Bletchley, Grahame-White had reduced the Frenchman's lead to 50 minutes. Excitement ran so high that position reports were telegraphed to the President of France, the German General Staff and the Czar of Russia, and bulletins were taken personally to King Edward VII at Buckingham Palace. In darkness Paulhan landed at Lichfield, Staffordshire, where he planned to stop the night, at 2010 hours. Five minutes earlier Grahame-White had put down at Roade, just 92km (57 miles) behind, and disclosed his intention to start again in darkness to overtake the Frenchman. No one had ever flown cross-country at night and, at best, it seemed a foolhardy idea.

However, Grahame-White was determined. At two in the morning, with a moon shining fitfully through rain clouds, he took off again, carrying mascots tied on by his mother and sister–a red velvet slipper, a bunch of heather, a violet ribbon and a golliwog. He was within 20 minutes' flying time of Lichfield when Paulhan finally became convinced that the impossible had happened and hurried to get his Farman into the air. Briefly, the two were airborne together, until fate again struck the Englishman, forcing him down near Polesworth in the Trent Valley, where he had been forced down a few days previously. He immediately called for three cheers for his rival, who landed at Manchester at 0532 hours, after battling against terrible conditions, the like of which he said he would not face again for a hundred thousand pounds. Grahame-White observed philosophically that since he had never had ten thousand pounds he did not know what he had missed by losing.

Public adulation

Although he had lost the prize, the gallant Englishman won public adulation as the first British hero of the air. Grahame-White was impersonated in variety halls and a waxwork effigy of him was displayed in Madame Tussaud's. He determined to popularise aviation and was soon a familiar figure at Brooklands in Surrey, where on one occasion a flight in his aeroplane was auctioned. The bidding finally stopped at 150 guineas, and Lady Abdy went aloft in Grahame-White's Farman, only to be unceremoniously deposited in the local sewage farm when the machine's Gnome engine failed.

Throughout the summer of 1910 Grahame-White took part in aviation meetings at Wolverhampton, Bournemouth (where the death of the Honourable Charles Rolls marred the event) and Blackpool, where he was paid a two thousand pound retainer for exhibition flights and carried the first military dispatches and airmails. In September 1910 he travelled to America to take part in the Boston-Harvard Aviation Meeting and the Gordon Bennett Trophy race at Belmont Park, New York. He won all the major prizes at both events and delighted the American public and Press. He even landed his Farman in the grounds of the White House to pay his respects to President Taft who, weighing fully 21 stone, wisely declined a ride.

Flying at Hendon

On his return, considerably the richer, Grahame-White acquired 89 hectares (220 acres) of pasture land at Hendon to create London's first aerodrome, and during the years 1911–1913 his weekend air displays proved to be the capital's most popular public attraction, drawing tens of thousands to watch races and stunting displays. It was at Hendon that Grahame-White gave the first demonstration of aerial bombing in May 1911 in the presence of Army and Navy senior staff and Prime Minister, Lloyd George. He repeated the exercise with a mocked-up warship the following year. He also pioneered night-flying with his Farman's wings illuminated by 120 light bulbs and organised an aerial tour of summer resorts in 1912, during which he gave a night-flying display over the Royal Yacht Victoria & Albert, anchored off Cowes, Isle of Wight. Grahame-White was the first Englishman to establish flying as a public attraction. He was a born showman and a shrewd entrepreneur whose name will forever be inextricably linked with Hendon Aerodrome, site of the Royal Air Force Museum.

When war broke out, Grahame-White was commissioned as a flight commander in the Royal Naval Air Service, with which he initiated night patrols over London in September 1914 and later participated in a mass aerial attack on German-held ports. Meanwhile the Grahame-White company had been granted war contracts and expanded from just 20 staff to more than 1,000. Grahame-White resigned from the Service to manage his business affairs and, having fallen foul of the authorities, was forced to go to France to look for postwar contracts. He sold aircraft, cars and prefabricated furniture until, disillusioned by his homeland, he sold Hendon to the Air Ministry and moved to California as a property dealer. He died in Nice, France in 1959 on his eightieth birthday.

Grahame-White flying a Henri Farman Series 20 at Hendon. Between 1911 and 1913 the aviator organized highly popular flying displays at this airfield, which became London's first aerodrome

JET INVENTOR

Air Commodore Sir Frank Whittle designed Britain's first jet aero engine

Frank Whittle, the inventor of the first British gas turbine jet engine to power an aircraft, commented: 'The idea of a jet-propelled aircraft first came to me as a cadet at Cranwell. When we had to write a science thesis, I chose as my subject the future development of aircraft.' However, to bring that idea to maturity was a frustrating and difficult task. Whittle's success was due to his considerable administrative and technical ability, combined with the tenacity of purpose to continue in the face of opposition.

Frank Whittle was born in Coventry on 1 June 1907. From infancy he showed an interest in things mechanical. Educated at Leamington College, he enlisted in the RAF in 1923 as a boy apprentice, going to No 1 School, Technical Training (Boys) at Cranwell. His ambition was, however, to be an officer. Upon finishing his course, he was one of the five apprentices who were selected annually for officer training at RAF College, Cranwell, and Whittle became a flight cadet in September 1926.

A speculative thesis

While in his final term at Cranwell in 1928, he suggested dispensing with the propeller and internal combustion engine and using a gas turbine engine or rockets to propel an aircraft by ejecting a stream of powerful gas. It was then believed that no aircraft, because of the limiting factors of propeller propulsion, would fly faster than 640 km/h (400 mph): Whittle suggested in his thesis that a jet-propelled aircraft would fly very much faster. The principle of jet propulsion had been known in embryonic form for centuries; gas turbine engines, which had been built for industry, had been suggested for aircraft propulsion, notably by A. A. Griffiths and H. H. Constant, but mainly as turboprops: Whittle's association of the gas turbine engine and the principle of jet propulsion was radically new. The only discouraging factor apparent was the unavailability of light metals which could withstand the white-hot operating temperatures and high stresses of such an engine. The thesis was published in the RAF Journal for 1928 and Whittle was awarded the coveted Abdy-Gerald-Fellowes Memorial Prize for aeronautical sciences. There was no further official reaction.

Whittle was posted as a pilot officer to No 111 Squadron, flying Armstrong Whitworth Siskin Mk IIIA fighters. He had been described officially at Cranwell as an 'exceptional to above average' but 'over-confident' pilot. On one occasion at Cranwell he had astounded observers by performing a low-level 'bunt' or outside loop in a Siskin, a type when considered unsafe for the manoeuvre. Afterwards he remarked: 'It wasn't difficult or even dangerous. You see, I'd worked it all out on a slide-rule'.

In 1929 Whittle attended the Flying Instructor course at the Central Flying School. He had continued to develop his ideas for jet-propelled aircraft and, while at CFS, his commanding officer encouraged him to present his ideas to the Air Ministry. Although politely interested, the Ministry turned Whittle down on the basis of the cost and difficulties involved in developing an engine of such an advanced and unproven concept. Whittle then approached

industrial companies, but none were interested. Discouraged, he filed a patent for the basic design–it was published world-wide in 1932 when he failed to renew it– and continued his RAF career. As a serving officer, his patent was subject to the provision that the Air Ministry could use its contents as it saw fit: this provision was later to cause Whittle great frustration.

In 1930, he became an instructor at No 2 Flying Training School, Digby, and was promoted to the rank of flying officer. In the following year he became a test pilot at the Marine Aircraft Experimental Establishment, Felixstowe, specialising in catapult work on floatplanes. He attended an Officer's Course of Engineering at RAF Henlow between 1932 and 1934, and in October of the latter year, he matriculated at Cambridge University, graduating in July 1937 with First Class Honours in the Mechanical Science Tripos, and was promoted to squadron leader. Thus, by the age of 30 he had a sound practical and theoretical training in aeronautical engineering.

Frank Whittle's career in the Royal Air Force ended in 1948, when he retired with the rank of air commodore. By this time, a jet-propelled aircraft had exceeded the speed of sound

Development frustrations

While at Cambridge, events moved favourably for Whittle's idea for jet propulsion. In 1935, through the agencies of two friends at Cambridge, J. C. B. Tinling and R. Dudley Williams, former RAF officers and partners in business, financial backing was obtained. Power Jets Limited was established in March 1936, with a capital of two thousand pounds, to exploit Whittle's idea. The executive abilities of these two men were crucial to the subsequent fortunes of Whittle's engine. Whittle began work on the design of the engine in June 1936. On 12 April 1937, he successfully ran the first British gas turbine jet propulsion engine, on a static test bench. The Air Ministry became interested now that it was seen to work, and seconded Whittle to the Special Duties List to continue development after his graduation from Cambridge.

On completion of the experimental engine, Power Jets moved to the Ladywood Works, a disused foundry on the outskirts of Lutterworth, Leicestershire, to continue testing. The results encouraged the Air Ministry to give Power Jets Ltd official backing: in March 1938 a contract was placed for an engine for flight trials in 1939. Later, the Gloster Aircraft Company was contracted to design and build an airframe to specification E28/39, the first British jet-propelled aircraft.

However, development was delayed by technical problems – mainly connected with power surging, and the unreliability and performance of rotary components and combustion – which led to modifications in design. These development problems were exacerbated by frustrations which largely arose because Whittle was dependent upon government interest, support, and above all, policy. A high-level report in March 1940 – much influenced by Air Chief Marshal Tedder, who was one of Power Jets Ltd's most forceful advocates – listed the jet engine among 'war-winning' first priority projects; Whittle's engine was put under full development at government expense, but no satisfactory method of helping Whittle's work was ever really achieved.

Power Jets Ltd was required to turn over the results of its research to the Air Ministry, in the first place because of the stricture on Whittle's original patent, and secondly

because of military requirements. However, the Air Ministry put this research at the disposal of the British Thomson-Houston Company (BTH) and the Rover Company, and gave them contracts to manufacture gas turbine jet engines, while denying Power Jets Ltd the rights to manufacture or subcontract for itself. This led to a prolonged debate: Whittle insisted that Power Jets Ltd required freedom to manufacture engines and should be primarily responsible for development, because that company had the greatest knowledge of gas turbine engine technology. He further insisted that to do this he required better facilities and better financing, more personnel and less restrictions.

The Air Ministry's policy, though deviously expressed, remained the same: Power Jets Ltd was purely for research and development, and manufacturing was to be contracted out at government, not Power Jets Ltd's, discretion. This resulted in ill-will between Power Jets, the government and the manufacturing companies, and in Whittle's opinion delayed development. However, the problems were resolved to the satisfaction of the Air Ministry when

Above left: the W.1 turbojet engine which powered the Gloster E28/39 on its first flight in 1941.
Left: Whittle was seconded to the Special Duties List to develop the jet engine.
Above right: Whittle (centre) is pictured with test pilot John Cunningham (left) and Frank Halford, designer of the Ghost jet engine which powered the de Havilland Comet, the world's first jet airliner.
Right: the first E28/39, together with the W.1, is preserved at the Science Museum in London.

Power Jets Ltd was nationalised in the interests of the war effort, in April 1944, becoming Power Jets (Research and Development) Ltd, and an associate of the National Gas Turbine Establishment.

First flight

Nevertheless, by early 1941, the Power Jets (Whittle) W.1 turbojet engine and the Gloster E28/39 were ready for mating and flight testing. Taxying trials took place successfully at Brockworth in April 1941. The first prototype E28/39 was powered by a single W.1 centrifugal-flow turbojet developing 390 kg (860 lb) static thrust. Piloted by Gloster's chief test pilot Flt Lt P. E. G. 'Gerry' Sayer, it first flew at dusk on 15 May 1941, appropriately at Cranwell, achieving 544 km/h (338 mph) at 4,570 m (15,000 ft) and remaining airborne for 17 minutes. It was the world's second jet aircraft to fly: the Heinkel He 178, which flew on 27 August 1939, had been the first jet aircraft to fly, powered by an engine designed by Hans von Ohain. Gloster's had already begun work on a fighter to be powered by two turbojets; this was the Meteor. The prototype Gloster Meteor first flew on 5 March 1943.

As a result of Power Jets' pressure on the Air Ministry, the company had been accommodated in a more spacious

and suitable factory at Whetstone, Leicestershire by the end of 1941, and had been given permission to manufacture up to 12 engines a year, for development purposes only. Further problems, particularly connected with the turbine blades and the compressor unit delayed engine production during 1942. Whittle was able to solve the turbine blade problem by considerably revising the theory on their function. However, BTH and Rover were unco-operative and even obstructive, resulting in several design developments and improvements by Whittle being introduced only after considerable delay. Many problems arose because of the Air Ministry's policy. BTH and Rover, while working with Power Jets on a production engine, were also engaged in designing and developing engines in competition with Power Jets Ltd, but based upon Whittle's research and designs, given to them by the Air Ministry. This produced unco-ordinated development, restricting Whittle's freedom to incorporate new developments and design changes. However, early in 1942, Power Jets entered into a third and, from the technical view, more fruitful partnership with Rolls-Royce.

Following a government decision to collaborate with the United States in jet engine development, three of Whittle's colleagues flew to the United States in September 1943, accompanied by a Whittle W.1 engine, to provide technical advice on the development of the first American jet engine. Whittle followed in July 1942, remaining until August. The General Electric Company was contracted to build the engines, and an airframe was contracted to the Bell Aircraft Corporation. The result was the Bell YP-59A, which first flew on 1 October 1942 at Lake Muroc.

In October 1944, Whittle's pioneering work brought him the highest award of the Council of the Royal Aeronautical Society, its Gold Medal. Whittle, a dark, slightly built, private individual, commented: 'I am completely embarrassed. Damn it, I wish I had been a doctor'.

In January 1946 Whittle resigned from Power Jets (R & D) Ltd because of continuing disagreements over the function and future of the company, which had been reduced to a handful of personnel; it was later merged with the Royal Aircraft Establishment, Farnborough. Whittle took up a post as Technical Adviser at the Ministry of Supply in June 1946. Over the next two years he made two lecture tours of the United States, but the years of overwork resulted in several months in hospital and Whittle was retired from the RAF with the rank of air commodore on 26 August 1948 on the grounds of ill-health. However, on 27 May 1948 it had been announced that the Royal Commission on Awards to Inventors, acting upon the initiative of the Air Ministry, had awarded Whittle one hundred thousand pounds free of tax for his pioneering work and, in July 1948, he was invested as a Knight of the British Empire by King George VI.

Whittle was employed as a technical adviser between 1948 and 1952 by the British Overseas Airways Corporation, but he had begun design work on a turbine drill for oil and natural gas prospecting. He worked as a technical adviser on the development of the Turbo-Drill with the Dutch Bataafsche Petroleum Maatschappij between 1953 and 1957 and Bristol Siddeley Engines between 1960 and 1966. He was associated with Rolls-Royce from 1966 until 1970, when he was appointed to the chair of Navair Research Professor at the US Naval Academy.

Fighting Over Finland

In 1939-40 the outnumbered Finnish air force gallantly resisted the Russian onslaught

A glance at the map of Northern Europe and Scandinavia immediately shows the strategic importance of Finland's position in relation to the Soviet Union. In 1939 the narrow Gulf of Finland, giving access to the important Russian city of Leningrad and to the island naval base of Kronstadt, was dominated to the north by Finland, and to the south by the independent states of Latvia, Lithuania and Estonia. At the eastern end of the gulf is a narrow strip of land – the Karelian Isthmus – between the sea and the vast Lake Ladoga. At the south of the isthmus, only a few miles from the Russo-Finnish border, is Leningrad.

Fearing Nazi aggression, the Russians had already sought to extend long-standing non-aggression treaties by seeking bases on Finnish islands in the gulf, or even the exchange of these for tracts of undeveloped land north of Lake Ladoga. These advances had been resolutely resisted by the Finns, as they had by the other independent Baltic states, until the signature of the Ribbentrop-Molotov Pact of August 1939 designated them as being in the Russian, rather than the German sphere of influence. Following the Russian involvement in the occupation of Poland the following month, Latvia, Lithuania and Estonia acceded to Soviet demands for military bases on

their soil. Although these new bases threatened the whole developed southern coast of Finland, including the capital Helsinki, and other ports like Turku and Kotka, the Finns refused increased demands for Soviet penetration.

All-out attack

However, now the Russians began to demand military bases on the mainland at Hanko Cape, islands in the gulf, and a northward adjustment of the border on the Karelian Isthmus, close to the city of Viipuri. This in itself would have meant the loss of the Mannerheim Line, Finland's main defensive position on the isthmus, and the most convenient and obvious invasion route into the country as a whole. No compromise offers were even considered, and on 29 November 1939 the Soviet Union broke off diplomatic relations with Finland, claimed that there had been border violations, and on the next day launched an all-out attack, including heavy air raids by Estonian-based bombers on Helsinki and other towns in the south. On the ground, ten Finnish divisions and two regiments faced 30 larger and better-equipped Russian divisions backed up by six tank brigades. Most of the strength of both adversaries was located around Lake Ladoga,

Below: licence-built examples of the Fokker C-X equipped two of the three Finnish reconnaissance units deployed in the army co-operation role. Bottom: December 1939 saw the introduction on the Finnish front of the Russian Polikarpov I-16 fighter, which was to serve with the biplane I-15bis

the Seventh Army in the Karelian Isthmus area had four regiments with 42 SB-2s and 94 I-I5bis fighters. Greatest strength was on the north Ladoga Lake sector with the Eighth Army, totalling ten flight regiments in five brigades with 280 SB-2s and 34 Ilyushin DB-3 bombers, 32 Polikarpov R-5 reconnaissance biplanes and 92 I-I5bis.

Estonian-based bombers

Clearly the small number of bombers and reconnaissance aircraft available to the Finns allowed little more than occasional nuisance and reconnaissance missions by single aircraft or pairs but, from the start, the fighters were to play an important part. Spread in flights throughout the southern part of the country, they had not received sufficient warning to intercept the raids of the first day of war, but early on 1 December when Estonian-based bombers again approached, they were ready. The first bomber, a DB-3, was brought down to crash-land in a snowdrift early in the morning by Lt Eino Luukkanean. This aircraft was later examined and the information derived regarding its unarmoured wing fuel tanks allowed many successful attacks to be made on others of the type. Before the day was out other flights had accounted for another DB-3 and eight SB-2s; the only loss was a single D XXI shot down by mistake by Finnish anti-aircraft fire. Even the Bulldogs were in action, claiming damage to one Russian fighter for the loss of one of their own.

Next day, however, a violent snowstorm began which was to last for nearly three weeks and put an end to all aerial activity. On the ground, operations continued; the main Russian attack on the Mannerheim Line met strong resistance and was halted by 6 December, but north of Lake Ladoga and up to the Ukhta area, deep advances

Above left: fourteen Bristol Blenheim bombers comprised Finland's main offensive strength at the start of the war. More aircraft were added later. Left: a number of Russian bombers were captured intact by Finnish forces. Below: many combat types of both sides were equipped with ski undercarriages for operation from snow. A Finnish Blenheim bomber is pictured. Bottom: more modern equipment did not reach the Finns in the shape of the Messerschmitt Bf 109G, 70 of which were delivered, until the Continuation War against Russia of 1941–44

particularly to the south on the Karelian Isthmus.

In the air the Finns had a small, but well-trained air force with 145 aircraft, 114 of which were operational. To co-operate with the army in Karelia were three reconnaissance squadrons, TLeLv 10, 12 and 14. The first two were equipped with Fokker C-X biplanes, built under licence from the Dutch, TLeLv 10 employing its aircraft in the dive-bomber role. TLeLv 14 had four C-Xs, but the bulk of its equipment comprised the older Fokker C-VEs. A fourth squadron, TLeLv 16, operated Blackburn Ripon IIF and Junkers K 43 floatplanes in detachments throughout the eastern part of the country for overwater operations. The main offensive strength rested on just two squadrons PLeLv 44 and 46, which between them comprised 14 licence-built Bristol Blenheim I bombers. For defence there were two fighter squadrons, HLeLv 24 and 26; the former and two flights of the latter had recently re-equipped with Fokker D XXI monoplanes – again built under licence. At the outbreak of war the two flights in HLeLv 26 which were equipped with these aircraft were attached to HLeLv 24, leaving only the third flight with the parent unit with ten elderly Bristol Bulldog IVA biplanes. Thirty-five Fiat G 50 monoplanes had been ordered from Italy, but were delayed on their way through Germany. Apart from trainers, first-line strength was completed by another eight floatplanes.

The Russians initially employed 696 aircraft in direct support of their armies, with a further 200 or so operating from Estonia, across the Gulf of Finland. In the far north the 14th Army at Murmansk was supported by two flight regiments with 18 ANT 35 (TB-3) heavy bombers, 14 Tupolev SB-2 medium bombers and 48 Polikarpov I-15bis biplane fighters. The Ninth Army in the Ukhta area had a single flight regiment with 18 TB-3s and 24 SB-2s, while

were made against the weak defences. The Russians were ill-equipped for winter campaigning, however, keeping to the few roads in unweildy, slow-moving convoys. Now small parties of highly-mobile Finns equipped with skis cut these convoys up into small sections and destroyed them. At Suomussalmi two full divisions were totally destroyed in December, while elsewhere terrible losses were sustained, the Russian advance on the whole Tola-jarvi–Suojarvi front being brought to a halt.

Russian air reinforcements were brought up when the weather improved in mid-December–including Poli-karpov I-16 monoplane fighters–but initially this did little to change the situation in their favour. Fokker D XXIs intercepting a raid on Saarenpää, south of Vyborg, on 19 December were able to claim 11 SB-2s and DB-3s, and a pair of I-16s without loss, while during patrols over the Karelian front on the 23rd, 11 more air-craft were shot down by the D XXIs for a single loss, an SB-2 also falling to a Bulldog. Two days later on Christmas Day, 3 Flight of HLeLv 24 was dispatched to Värtsilä to support troops of IV Corps north of Ladoga, where two of the pilots at once brought down four SB-2s; four more bombers fell to other members of the squadron still in the south, and by the end of the year the D XXIs had been credited with 50 victories, including one R-5, eight I-16s, two I-15bis biplanes and 39 bombers.

The new year started with further combats as the Finns counter-attacked both on the isthmus and north of the lake. The most notable combat of the war occurred on 6 January 1940 when eight DB-3s raided the Utti area. One was shot down by Lt Per-Erik Sovelius, the other seven being caught after they had bombed Kuopio by Lt Jorma Sarvanto. Although his fighter was riddled by return fire,

Sarvanto persevered single-handed until he had shot down six of the lightly-armoured bombers. Sovelius then appeared at the scene of the battle and dispatched the remaining aircraft.

Help was now at hand, most immediately from neigh-bouring Sweden. A volunteer unit, Flygflottilj 19, was sent to operate in the Lake Kemi area against the Soviet Ninth Army. This arctic area had until now enjoyed no air support and the Swedes were most welcome. Four Hawker Hart reconnaissance-bombers and 12 Gloster J-8 Gladiator Mark Is arrived under the command of Major Hugo Beckhammer on 11 January 1940. Following the bombing of their airfield soon after arrival, they were detached in flights to several strips, but they had already claimed their first victim–an I-15bis on 12 January, shot down by Vänr Jacobi.

Top: British aid to the beleaguered Finns included a gift of 10 Gloster Gladiator Mark II biplane fighters.
Centre: the Soviet Tupolev SB-2 was the most widely-deployed medium bomber of the Winter War.
Above: a Soviet-built Polikarpov I-153 which, having been captured by Finnish forces, was employed against its country of origin

Aid from abroad

Finland's 'David and Goliath' struggle had evinced much sympathy in the Western World, and aid was on the way from Britain and France. During December the French began shipment of a gift of 30 Morane-Saulnier MS 406 fighters, while the British presented 24 Gloster Gauntlet Mark IIs and 10 Gladiator Mark IIs to the Finns, also selling them an additional 20 Gladiators and 12 Bristol Blenheim Mark IV bombers. From Sweden came a single Douglas DC-1 which was to be used as a bomber, three Fokker C-VDs, two Koolhoven FK 52s and three J 6A Jaktfalk fighters. Also during December the first two Fiat G 50s arrived. On 13 January Captain Olavi Ehrnrooth shot down an SB-2 while flying the first of the Fiats, and was to add another to his score on 29th.

Throughout January the Russians on the Karelian Isthmus remained quiescent as the commanders were

During January, 11 of the Blenheim Mark IVs had arrived and been handed to PLeLv 46, which passed its remaining Mark Is to PLeLv 44, strengthening the two units. The new aircraft suffered from the increase in Russian aerial activity, however, and by the end of the month four had been lost and three damaged on operations. Meanwhile a number of HLeLv 26's pilots had returned from their attachment to HLeLv 24 to convert to the first 12 Gladiators to reach the unit, and at the beginning of February the remaining Bulldogs were relegated to training, where they were later joined by the Gauntlets and Jaktfalk aircraft.

The Gladiators were first in action on 2 February, proving that they had the manoeuvrability to cope with the Russian fighters. Of four initial victories, two were I-16s and one an I-153 biplane. The Russians now launched a massive new offensive against the Mannerheim Line and,

Below left: stripped of its wings, a Russian bomber brought down by anti-aircraft fire is removed. Bottom left: the Soviet Union employed Lavochkin's single-engined fighter series for battlefield air superiority. Below: among the aircraft captured by the Finns during the Winter War was this Soviet Scha-2 seaplane. Bottom: an air raid on the Finnish capital, Helsinki, on 9 December 1939

replaced and reinforcements brought up. Soviet air strength had now risen to around 1,500 aircraft, however, and mid-January brought a resumption of aerial activity. On the 17th, nine SB-2s were claimed by HLeLv 24, while the Swedes claimed two I-15bis fighters. Two days later the D XXIs added five more. On the 20th, pilots from HLeLv 24 shot down eight more SB-2s, one falling to Sgt Pentti Tilli as his fifth victory. However, the next moment he was attacked by six fighters and shot down – the first serious loss for the fighters. That same day five more SBs were claimed, four of them falling to Lt E. Itävueri, while a C-X pilot of TLeLv 12, Sgt Martila, shot down another to make this the most costly day yet for the Russians. Next day HLeLv 24 was ordered to avoid fights with Russian fighters if possible, as the D XXI was proving to be somewhat outclassed by the I-16s and I-15bis.

while this made but slow progress, sheer weight of numbers gradually wore the Finns down. The D XXIs and Gladiators were much in evidence during the month, many combats being fought, and the Blenheims and C-Xs were also used regularly for attacking Russian concentrations and supply lines. The new Gladiators achieved considerable success initially, but not without losses; on 13 February WO Oiva Tuominen shot down three SB-2s and an R-5, and shared another SB, while Lt Ulrich shot down two I-15bis fighters from a total 'bag' for the day of eight aircraft. Two Gladiators were lost. More HLeLv 26 pilots returned to HLeLv 24 for the re-equipment of the third flight with Fiat G 50s, while a new unit, HLeLv 28, was formed with the first MS 406s to arrive. The latter were first in action on 17 February when two large bomber formations were turned back when attempting to bomb troops at Vyborg; three were shot down and three damaged by D XXIs, one shot down and one damaged by an MS 406 and one damaged by a G 50.

Clashes with the enemy were occurring daily now, and on the 20th four units were in action; two bombers were

claimed by HLeLv 24, two by HLeLv 26's Gladiators and one by a Swedish Gladiator, while the MS 406s of HLeLv 28 in their first major combat shot down four more; one Gladiator was lost. By now the further 18 Gladiators had arrived, and one flight of these aircraft was detached to reinforce 3/HLeLv 24 north of Ladoga. Here, on 25 February six Gladiators and nine D XXIs became involved in a big dogfight, during which the Gladiators shot down four aircraft but lost three of their own number.

Invaders' victory

On 26 February the G 50 was introduced to front-line service with HLeLv 26. After attacking and damaging a DB-3 from a formation of five, Gladiators were seen in combat with two I-16s, and the G 50s joined in. Both Russian fighters were shot down, one by each type. On the 27th, however, one Fiat was shot down in combat and the pilot killed. It was now intended that the Gladiators should be passed to Flight Regiment 1 for tactical reconnaissance duties as soon as sufficient G 50s were available to re-equip HLeLv 26, but on 29 February an event occurred which speeded this change. A strong force of I-16s attacked 3HLeLv 24's base just as the D XXIs and Gladiators were taking off. One D XXI and five Gladiators were shot down, the former flown by six-victory ace Lt Tatu Huhanantti, who was killed.

By 1 March the Russians were nearing the town of Viipuri, but at that stage launched troops across the frozen Viipuri Bay to outflank the Finnish defences. Air combat was now left mainly to the G 50s and MS 406s, the D XXIs being assigned to escort the Blenheims and strafe the

Russian forces on the ice. During this last period of the war, interceptions of the Blenheims became more frequent, as Russian air strength was now up to over 2,000 aircraft. Twelve more Blenheim Is had been bought from England during February, and a new unit – PLeLv 48 – formed, while 44 Brewster B 239 fighters were on their way from the United States. However, they were not to arrive in time to be flown by HLeLv 22, formed mainly from foreign volunteers. Air gunners in Blenheims had claimed damage to attacking fighters on several occasions, but during March were to claim four actually shot down, including three I-153s on 10 March, two of them by one gunner. In the north, the Swedes continued to gain successes, one pilot shooting down two SB-2s on 7 March, while on the 10th the only four-engined TB-3 to be shot down was claimed as Flygflottilj 19's 12th and last victory. On the next day G 50s and MS 406s shot down four DB-3s during the last combats of the war. Viipuri had been held, but the position was hopeless, and on 13 March an armistice was agreed, ceding large areas of Karelia and northern Finland to the invaders.

Below left: buildings in Mekkeli are pictured after a Soviet raid on civilian targets in January 1940. Below: contemporary Finnish propaganda posters emphasise the importance of air power in the Winter War

Birth of the Aeroplane

In 1903 Wilbur and Orville Wright made the first powered, heavier-than-air flights

The Wright brothers are spoken of together with the force of legend, but Wilbur and Orville were distinct and contrasting personalities, the one outliving the other by 36 years. Recent research such as J. E. Walsh's *First Flight* published in the United States in 1975 asserts that Wilbur's was the primary inventive genius and Orville supplied the alert complementary criticism, considerable mechanical skill and piloting ability.

Wilbur Wright grew up in the midwest of the United States in the late nineteenth century. He was born on a farm near Millville, near New Castle, Indiana on 16 April 1867 and Orville was four years his junior. The brothers' home atmosphere was religious and encouraged intellectual inquiry. Mrs Wright had the knack of mending things and some competence in mathematics. Wilbur and Orville lived, played and worked together but their formal education did not go beyond high school. Wilbur's plan to go to Yale Divinity School ended when a disastrous blow from an ice-hockey stick smashed his teeth and jaw. For several years he remained at home, rather intense and reserved, a semi-invalid; he concentrated on reading, especially in science. Orville, voluble and outgoing, dropped out of high school, becoming a printer's apprentice.

Wing warping concept

In December 1892 the brothers opened a small bicycle shop for repairs and rental in Dayton, Ohio. The business prospered and they began to make their own brands of bicycles. The money earned later enabled them to indulge their growing enthusiasm for aviation. It was perhaps an article which they read on Otto Lilienthal in 1894 which really excited them. Lilienthal had made careful records of his experiments with glides on bird-like wings and his work on wing surfaces and air pressures was especially

intriguing to the young engineers. The death of Lilienthal in a gliding crash in 1896 was a sobering reminder of the dangerous element into which they were venturing. Wilbur in true scientific spirit wrote to the Smithsonian Institution for information on aeronautics. The publications suggested to him for reading included works by Dr Samuel P. Langley who later became the director of the Smithsonian. Also included was Octave Chanute's *Progress in Flying Machines*. Both Langley and Chanute, the latter a successful construction engineer, were to have marked influence on the Wright's future in aviation.

The months spent watching birds in flight during his semi-seclusion had led Wilbur to diagnose the primary problem of manned flying as achieving control. Endless discussions at home and in their workshop soon led the brothers to practical design of a glider. They discarded the concept of flapping wings and, using Lilienthal's tables, arrived at the concept of wing warping, torsion or, as it

Below: the Wrights' first powered aircraft, the Flyer I, pictured in 1903. The aircraft was test-flown at Kill Devil Hill in North Carolina. Bottom: the first flight by a powered aircraft. The Wright Flyer I took off and sustained controlled flight under its own power in the mid-morning of Thursday 17 December 1903 at Kill Devil Hill, piloted by Orville Wright. The Wrights made four successful flights between 10.35 am and noon

later became, aileron control. This increased the angle of attack on one wingtip and decreased it on the other. Their first model at Dayton was a kite and, after testing an elevator in front and at the rear, they became convinced that both lateral and longitudinal control were possible.

The next stage was to build a full-size, man-carrying glider and to try it out somewhere with constant wind and with the utmost privacy. Wind records were obtained from the Weather Bureau in Washington and they chose a site near the Kill Devil Hill Weather Station at Kitty Hawk on the coast of North Carolina. In the years from 1900 to 1903 the brothers made annual journeys to set up primitive accommodation in the dunes of that bleak coast. Their first glider was flown as a kite, having a wingspan of 5m (17ft). However, before returning to Dayton both brothers essayed free glides from the slopes of Kill Devil Hill. They lay in a prone position athwart the lower wing of the glider which landed on sledge-like skids.

Wind tunnel tests

In 1901 a new glider with a wingspan of 6·7m (22ft) was tested. The camber of the wings was varied and shapes were tested against Lilienthal's tables of air pressures. Their performances led them to question much of what passed as scientific data in the available literature. In true practical engineers' fashion they constructed their own simple wind tunnel back at Dayton to examine wing shapes and to measure lift/drag ratios. By 1902, the brothers had incorporated their knowledge of aerodynamics into a new glider with a wingspan of 9·7m (32ft) which was about six times the previous chord. The glider also had twin vertical vanes at the rear as well as a front elevator and the wing warping mechanism was actuated by the pilot's hips resting in a cradle on the lower wing. The combination of warp and rudder control was an advance. They had nearly solved the problem of control in all three planes of flight. With the business acumen and caution which characterised their later enterprises, the brothers applied for a US patent covering the drawings and specifications in March 1903.

Their assistant, shopkeeper and mechanic in Dayton was Charles Taylor who now set to work to help them build a motor for the glider. No commercial automobile engine was available at the required weight, so they built their own and eventually achieved a power output of about 12 horse-power. When it came to propellers they found again that previous attempts had been inefficient and they designed and machined their own from three laminations of spruce, the tips being covered with a thin layer of canvas. The 'Flyer' of 1903 was to be driven by two propellers 2·6m (eight feet, six inches) long rotating in opposite directions and driven by heavy-duty chains linked to the motor.

First flight at Kitty Hawk

The Wright brothers were spurred on by reports that, after several spectacular flops, Langley was about to launch another powered machine from a houseboat on the Potomac River, but they did not reach Kitty Hawk until the autumn. As in previous years, Wilbur and Orville shared the tedium of humping and carrying their equipment and stores on the difficult journey by land and water to the Kill Devil Hill sands. They shared the domestic chores, the frequent repairs after crashes and the excitement and the danger of piloting. The year 1903 was to prove the high noon of their experiments; after tossing a coin Wilbur was the first to attempt to fly their machine from a trolley mounted on a track made up of four lengths of timber, each 4·6m (15ft) long, set end to end on edge, the top being sheathed with an iron strip. This was on 14

December and neither brother considered the trial a legitimate flight. However, on 17 December in front of witnesses from the nearby weather station, Orville made history when he made a flight of 37m (120ft) in twelve seconds against a 43km/h (27mph) wind. Later that day both brothers made longer flights.

The next phase of the Wrights' activity was a bewildering one. Wilbur was determined on the one hand to keep the 'Flyer' specifications secret and to keep the press at bay—especially photographers—on the other hand, however, he wished to realise the commercial possibilities of their machine and to sell it, if possible, in an international market. The following year was spent in developing their 'Flyer No 2' at Huffman's Prairie near their home town. A catapult device was made to give an impetus launch, a new engine was tested, and the brothers refined their piloting techniques. At the end of the year both could manoeuvre the machine in turns and on an 'S' course.

Wilbur offered the machine to the United States War Department, but was unwilling to agree to close inspection or demonstration of the machine before a contract was signed. In 1904 Wilbur received a visit from Colonel J. E. Capper from England and he now offered to sell the machine to the British War Office. They eventually replied indicating interest, but seeking to have more details from first-hand observation of the machine in flight. The Wrights then approached the French, but protracted negotiations ended when the brothers decided that the speed, height and carrying capacity demanded of them were

Above: the Flyer III was the first practical aeroplane, being capable of lengthy flights under full control. The Wrights' system of controls enabled their aircraft to turn, bank and fly in a circle.
Right: the brothers' desire to find military application for their aircraft was tempered by a reluctance to disclose design details. Nevertheless, military biplanes like the pictured example were flying by 1910

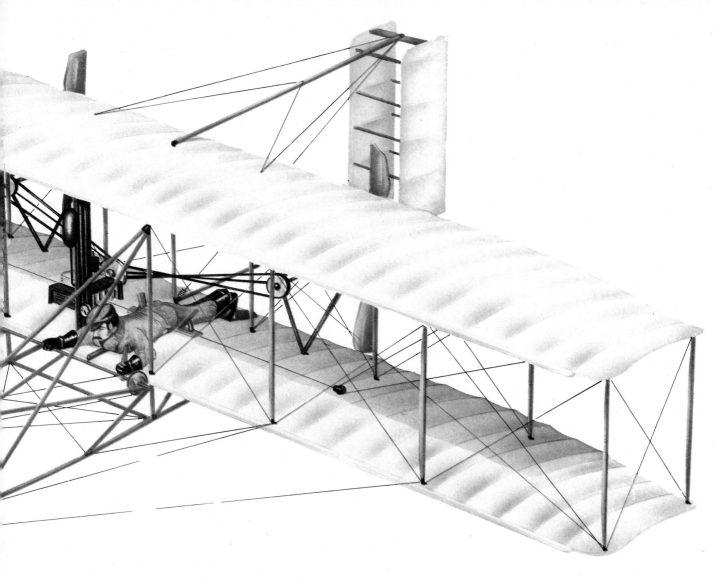

2351

too stringent at that time. In the meantime careful photographs and independent testimony of the machine's capabilities were made available to the American and foreign press. In France especially, the enthusiasm for flying was reinforced by the realisation that others were also on the verge of proving indigenous powered machines. At the end of 1906 the Wrights co-opted the expert aid of Charles R. Flint, who was one of the leading international arms dealers. He had contacts in London, Berlin and St Petersburg. Through the strenuous efforts of Lady Jane Taylor, his London contact, Flint made approaches to R. B. Haldane at the War Office and to Lord Tweedmouth at the Admiralty. However, both departments decided not to pursue the offer from the Americans at that time. Wilbur's cautious commercialism made clinching a deal at government level a very difficult task.

Years of success

It was not until 1908 that the Wrights' bid to furnish a flying machine for the US War Department was accepted. The price was twenty-five thousand dollars. In the same year Lazare Weiller agreed to a contract with the Wrights to form a company in France to build their aeroplanes. Meanwhile, the Wrights had made offers to the German, Italian, Japanese and Russian ministers of war and had applied for patents to cover their inventions in the main European countries. In 1908 Wilbur went to France where he was in the company of such aviators as Leon Delagrange, Henri Farman and Louis Blériot. His demonstrations of flying at Le Mans and later at Pau evoked from Réne Gasnier the exclamation, 'compared with the Wrights, we are as children'. The kings of England, Italy and Spain were among the spectators of his successful flights at Pau. Back in the United States Orville was carrying out the proving flights required by the Army contract at Fort Meyer. He too received great acclaim but sadly was involved in the first fatal crash of a powered flying machine. He was severely injured and his passenger, Lt Thomas E. Selfridge, was killed when their machine dived into the ground from a height of 22m (72ft).

Nevertheless, these were days and months of triumph and recognition and medals, awards and prizes were numerous. Among them were the Gold Medal of the Aero Club of the United Kingdom and, later the Gold Medal of the Aeronautical Society of Great Britain. Recognition by governments also followed; a White House ceremony to award gold medals was held on 10 June 1909. Wilbur electrified millions who gazed upwards from New York's streets and waterfronts as he circled the waist of the Statue of Liberty and flew over the *Lusitania* to land back on Governors Island as part of the New York City anniversary celebrations; Orville was earning praise and more fame by his flying demonstrations in Berlin.

The commercial interests of the Wrights were also prospering; a contract was made with the Short Brothers in Britain to construct six Wright machines at one thousand pounds each, a Wright machine manufacturing company was formed in Germany and in the United States on 22 November 1909 the Wright Company was formed with Wilbur as president and Orville as a vice-president. However, the first of many law suits was also begun to challenge Glenn H. Curtiss for infringing the patents of the Wright brothers in his Curtiss aeroplanes. In 1910 the Wright Aeroplane factory at Dayton was opened, but on 30 May 1912 Wilbur died of typhoid fever.

After his brother's death, Orville remained a respected and honoured figure in US aviation and business circles. However, in 1914 he fell out with the Smithsonian Institution which in its annual report claimed that 'the Aerodrome of Samuel P. Langley was the first aeroplane capable of sustained free flight with a man'. The feud resulted in the 1903 Wright aeroplane being shipped out of the United States in 1928 for exhibition in the Science Museum. It was eventually returned to the Smithsonian in 1948, after the Institution had published a retraction and apology in 1942. Orville lived to see a major air force base given the family name–it is now the home of the USAF Museum–and memorials erected at many places including Pau and at the Kill Devil Hill site in North Carolina. He died on 30 January 1948 at the age of 77.

Above: a Wright A was tested at Fort Meyer, near Washington between September 1908 and July 1909 by the US Signal Corps. On 30 July the US Army bought a Wright A, which thus became the first aeroplane to be procured for military use.
Above right: the Wright Baby Grande, fitted with the only Wright V-8 engine to be flown, is pictured in 1910.
Right: the Wright four-cylinder engine which powered the 1903 Flyer I.
Below right: the Wright engine which, installed in the Flyer I, drove the two pusher propellers via sprocket chains.
Far right: the Memorial erected to commemorate the Wright Brothers' achievements at Kitty Hawk, near the site of their first powered flight

Backbone of the Fighter Regiments

Yakovlev fighters were built in greater numbers than any other Soviet warplanes of this type

Alexander Sergeevich Yakovlev is the last of the pre-war generation of Soviet aircraft designers, and together with A. N. Tupolev and A. I. Mikoyan was one of the most successful. He is best-known as a designer of trainer and fighter aircraft and, latterly, of passenger transports. Twice a Hero of Socialist Labour, Yakovlev has received six State Prizes and been awarded seven Orders of Lenin in addition to receiving the French Croix de la Légion d'Honneur in recognition of the close association between his design bureau and the Free French air force during World War II.

A. S. Yakovlev was born on 19 March 1906 in Moscow where his father was manager of a department of the Nobel Petroleum Company. He was educated in Moscow and failed to get into the Zhukovskyi Air Force Academy when he applied in 1924, subsequently taking a mechanic's job in the Academy workshops. Yakovlev played a leading part in his local Young Communist Pioneers and Oso-viakhim, the voluntary society for aviation, and it was Osoviakhim that provided the backing for his first three light aircraft. Prior to this, he had been a regular attender at the All-Union Gliding Meetings in the Crimea since their inauguration in 1923, and monoplane gliders designed by him were flown at the 1924 and 1925 Meetings. It was, however, his first powered aircraft which gained him entry to the Zhukovskyi Academy in 1927. This was the VVA-3 (Air Force Academy-3) which was built in the workshops of the Zhukovskyi Air Force Academy during the winter and spring of 1926–27.

Moscow to Sevastopol

The VVA-3 was a small Moth-type two-seat biplane of all-wooden construction powered by a 60hp Blackburn Cirrus engine. In June 1927, a month after the first flight, the VVA-3 established class records for distance and speed when it was flown from Moskow to Sevastopol – 1,240 km (770 miles) in 15 hours 30 minutes. The pilot was Yu. Piontkovskyi, who later became Yakovlev's chief test pilot, and Yakovlev himself was navigator/mechanic. Both men received prizes for their achievement and Yakovlev was accepted into the Academy. The VVA-3 is better-known by the designation AIR-1, AIR representing the initials of A. I. Rykov, Lenin's successor as Chairman of the Council of People's Commissars from 1924 to 1929. This tribute was an astute move on the part of an ambitious young man, as was the retrospective change to Ya-1 when Rykov became one of the victims of the pre-war purges in 1938.

Yakovlev continued to design and build lightplanes while he was a student. Six AIR-2s were built between 1928 and 1931. The AIR-2 was similar to the AIR-1 but was powered by a variety of engines, the most successful and most powerful of which was the 85hp Siemens. In the meantime, using his glider experience, Yakovlev built a two-seat parasol-wing monoplane, the AIR-3. This collected two international records in its class and was developed as the AIR-4 of 1930 and AIR-8.

The AIR-5 completed in 1931 was the first Yakovlev lightplane to have an enclosed cabin. It was also the first

of his many designs which were of mixed wood and metal construction; welded steel tube was used for the fuselage, duralumin for the tail unit and the wings were wooden throughout. Even Yakovlev's wartime fighters followed this formula. A four/five-seater high-wing monoplane, the AIR-5 was the original ancestor of the postwar Yak-12. It was powered by a 200hp Wright J-4A 7-cylinder air-cooled radial engine which gave it a maximum speed of 193 km/h (120 mph) at sea level and allowed a range of 1,000 km (620 miles).

Central Design Bureau

Despite good performance and being simple to fly, the AIR-5 did not go into production because no Soviet equivalent of the Wright J-4A existed. It was, however, scaled down to fit Shvetsov's 100hp M-11 five-cylinder radial engine. This version, designated AIR-6, was completed in May 1932 at the Menzhinskyi factory, which normally produced military aircraft. A. S. Yakovlev had graduated from the Zhukovskyi Academy in 1931 and joined the Central Design Bureau (TsKB) under N. N. Polikarpov. At his own request he did not work as a designer but as an engineering supervisor, which enabled him to have his AIR-5, AIR-6 and AIR-7 sportsplanes built at the factory. The AIR-6 was a two/three-seat cabin monoplane, with dimensions similar to those of the AIR-5 but a take-off weight of only 900 kg (1,980 lb) compared with 1,390 kg (3,060 lb) for the AIR-5. Maximum speed was 162 km/h (101 mph) at sea level, and range 650 km (400 miles). A total of 468 were built including twenty of an ambulance version.

Polikarpov's I-5 single-seat biplane fighter was in production at the Menzhinskyi factory at this time. It was powered by a 480 hp M-22 radial engine and had a maximum speed of 252 km/h (157 mph) at 2,000 m (6,560 ft), and Yakovlev was inspired to build a two-seat sportsplane, with the same engine, which would be faster. The result was the AIR-7 for which he had estimated a speed of 320 km/h (200 mph).

The AIR-7 was the first of Yakovlev's designs which, despite external bracing wires, displayed the clean lines which his name was to become associated with. The crew of two was accommodated in tandem under a long glasshouse canopy, and main undercarriage legs and wheels were enclosed in wide-chord spats. The AIR-7 achieved 325 km/h (202 mph) on its first flight in 1932 and eventually a maximum speed of 332 km/h (206 mph). The authorities, however, did not take kindly to such private-enterprise activities and following a forced-landing in a railway freightyard when the AIR-7 was being demonstrated to air force officials, Yakovlev was debarred from the factory. He was, however, able to get support from Party officials and as a result he and his new Light Aviation design team moved into an old bed factory on the Leningradskyi Prospekt which today is the design bureau's headquarters and houses a private museum. Here 468 AIR-6 lightplanes, including 20 of an ambulance version, were produced from 1933 to 1936.

Right: the AIR-10 was built in large numbers for the air force and flying clubs.
Above far right: the AIR-18 introduced a retractable undercarriage and was modified from the UT-1 of 1936.
Far right: variously known as the Ya-22 and BB-22, the Yak-4 light bomber flew in 1939.
Below: the UT-1 was a manoeuvrable single-seat aerobatic trainer, some 1,241 examples of which were produced

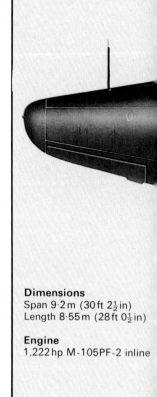

Dimensions
Span 9·2 m (30 ft 2½ in)
Length 8·55 m (28 ft 0½ in)

Engine
1,222 hp M-105PF-2 inline

Sportsplanes and trainers

The new design bureau produced eleven sportsplanes and trainers between 1936 and 1939. The AIR-9, designed for an Aviavnito (Aviation Scientific-Research Technical Society) competition for an M-11-powered two-seat trainer with an enclosed cabin, was based on the AIR-7 and completed in 1934. An open-cockpit development completed the following year was designated AIR-10. Both aircraft took part in the competition over a 500 km (311 mile) course, which was won by the AIR-10. This subsequently entered production as the UT-2 (Primary trainer-2) and a total of 7,243 was built between 1937 and 1944. With the Po-2 the UT-2 shared the initial training of all Soviet air force pilots up to the end of World War II.

The UT-1 – which carried the design bureau designation AIR-14 – was a scaled-down single-seat aerobatic trainer first built in 1936, of which 1,241 were produced. Astonishingly, some flying school UT-1s were flown on offensive operations in the Caucasus in 1942. Equipped with two 7·62 mm ShKAS machine guns and four RS rocket projectiles, they attacked enemy aerodromes, supplies and communications; one Black Sea Fleet pilot lived through 140 sorties to tell the tale.

An AIR-10 powered by a 120 hp Renault inline engine which was built in 1937 was designated AIR-20 and won a sporting event that year. Another, designated AIR-12, was modified for a women's lightplane distance record and had a retractable undercarriage and flush transparent cover over the navigator's position which was in front of the pilot's cockpit.

Two other pre-war Yakovlev sportsplanes were in the Percival Gull class. These were the AIR-11 and AIR-16. The AIR-11 of 1936 was a three-seat cabin monoplane powered by a 120 hp de Havilland Gipsy Major six-cylinder inline engine, which used the same wings, tail unit and undercarriage as the AIR-10 but had a widened fuselage. It had a maximum speed of 206 km/h (128 mph) and a range of 720 km (477 miles). Only one was built and was given to S. V. Ilyushin in 1937. Ilyushin was severely injured following a forced landing in the AIR-11 which resulted from engine failure when a mechanic omitted to refill the oil tank. The AIR-16 of 1937 had a more powerful 220 hp Renault engine and carried an additional passenger, but was otherwise similar.

Yakovlev produced his first multi-engined aircraft in 1938. This was the AIR-17 (UT-3) three-seat crew trainer which was powered by two 220 hp MV-6 (Soviet built Renault) inline engines. It was followed in 1939 by the similarly powered AIR-19, which was an eight/ten seat passenger transport and was the pre-war inspiration of the Yak-6. In the event, neither the AIR-17 nor AIR-19 was adopted to go into production.

Inspiration from abroad

During trips abroad immediately before World War II, Yakovlev had been able to see a number of the latest high-speed aircraft in France, Britain and Germany and, in particular, had been impressed by the Supermarine Spitfire and Messerschmitt Bf 109. Work on the Ya-22 or BB-22 (short-range bomber) had started in 1938 and the prototype was completed early in 1939. The same method of construction was used for the BB-22 as for Yakovlev's

Top left: despite the upheaval caused by the evacuation of the aircraft industry in 1941, over 8,700 Yak-1s were produced in 1940–43. Above left: the first Yak 1 was rolled out on 1 January 1940, leaving the ground on its maiden flight in March. The small, heavily-armed fighter was to give stalwart service during the early war years

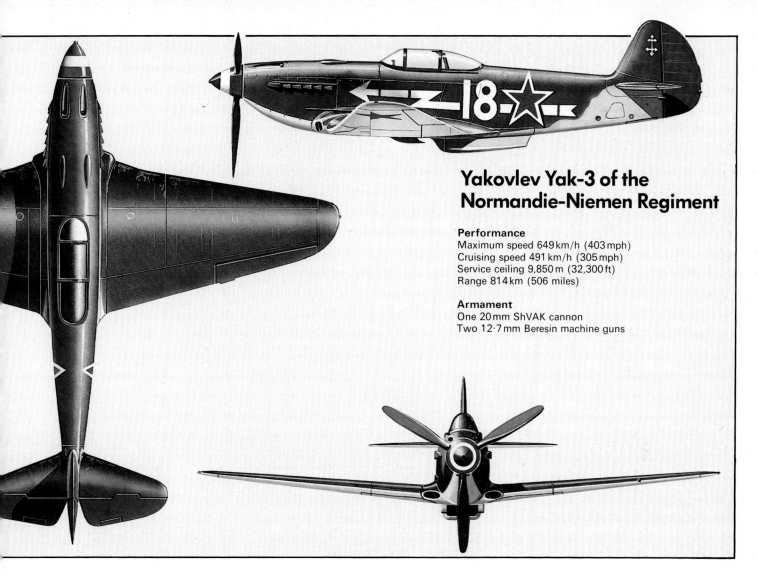

Yakovlev Yak-3 of the Normandie-Niemen Regiment

Performance
Maximum speed 649 km/h (403 mph)
Cruising speed 491 km/h (305 mph)
Service ceiling 9,850 m (32,300 ft)
Range 814 km (506 miles)

Armament
One 20 mm ShVAK cannon
Two 12·7 mm Beresin machine guns

pre-war sportsplanes. It had wooden wings, a plywood monocoque forward and centre fuselage, a rear fuselage of steel tube construction and duralumin tail unit. It was powered by two 960 hp M-103 12-cylinder liquid-cooled engines which gave the BB-22 prototype, which had a cleaner cabin outline than production aircraft, a maximum speed of 567 km/h (352 mph). There were two 7·62 mm ShKAS machine guns for defence and up to 600 kg (1,320 lb) of bombs could be carried. Flight tests began in 1939 and the BB-22 was demonstrated over Red Square on May Day that year. Yakovlev was awarded the Order of Lenin, a ZIS car and one hundred thousand roubles in recognition of his work.

A photographic reconnaissance version designated at the same time was designated R-12; another variation, the I-29 fighter, was additionally armed with two 20 mm cannon. However, only the bomber, redesignated Yak-4, was produced, with two 1,100 hp M-105R engines. Yakovlev, who was just beginning his working partnership with V. K. Klimov, received the first of the new M-105 engines for the Yak-4 and Yak-1 as the result of Stalin's personal intervention in the matter.

Ministerial appointment
In 1940, Yakovlev was appointed a Deputy Minister of the Aviation Industry. On 1 January 1940 the prototype of his I-26 (Ya-26, Yak-1) was rolled out, although the first flight was delayed until March. The prototype, like the Spitfire and Bf 109 which had inspired it, had very clean lines and achieved a maximum speed of almost 600 km/h (370 mph) during flight tests. Like Mitchell and Messer-

schmitt, Yakovlev believed in the small, lightweight, high-powered, heavily-armed fighter, together with manoeuvrability and simplicity in construction which was a feature of almost all Soviet military aircraft. The method of building the Yak-1 was exactly the same as that used for the pre-war trainers and Yak-2/4; it was powered by a 1,050 hp M-105P 12-cylinder inline engine which had a cannon gun mounted between the cylinder banks.

A pre-production batch of aircraft was produced almost simultaneously with the prototype and 64 Yak-1s had been produced by the end of 1940. Engine problems resulted in the introduction of the enlarged oil radiator intake under the nose which became a familiar feature of the series, and despite the upheaval caused by the evacuation of the aircraft industry in 1941, 8,721 Yak-1s were produced between 1940 and 1943. The type was replaced on the production lines of one factory by the Yak-7, which had been developed from the Yak-1 via the Yak-7V two-seat conversion trainer. In fact, conversion trainers of almost all Soviet military aircraft have been produced since the UTI-4 trainer version of the I-16, which at one time accounted for a quarter of the I-16 production.

Multi-purpose fighter
Further modification led to the Yak-9, which began as a Yak-7 with a steel alloy wing spar. The new wing was lighter and left more room for fuel so that range was increased. When the Yak-9 went into production, the rear fuselage was cut down and an all-round vision canopy fitted. The Yak-9 of 1943 was powered by a 1,240 hp VK-105PF engine which gave it a maximum speed of

600 km/h (370 mph) at 3,500 m (11,480 ft). Range was increased to 900 km (560 miles) on the standard series, and long-range versions such as the Yak-9DD at the end of the war had a maximum range of up to 2,200 km (1,370 miles). Fighter-bomber, anti-tank, reconnaissance and trainer Yak-9s were produced; regiments often had not only different variants of the Yak-9, but Yak-1s and Yak-7s among their equipment at any one time.

The Yak-9 had developed into a multi-purpose fighter and the design team went back to the Yak-1 to develop a lightweight low-level interceptor and produced the Yak-3. Aerodynamic improvements included re-siting the oil radiator at the wing centre-section, new engine exhausts, sealing gaps in the airframe surface and polishing the wings. With a 1,290 hp VK-105PF-2 engine, the Yak-3 had a maximum speed of 655 km/h (407 mph) at 3,300 m (10,820 ft). It entered service in 1943 and was popular with the French pilots of the Normandie-Niemen Regiment, who had previously flown earlier Yaks.

All-metal versions of both the Yak-3 and Yak-9 entered production at the end of the war and the Yak-9P, powered by a 1,700 hp VK-107A had a maximum speed of 698 km/h (434 mph) at 5,500 m (18,045 ft). The first all-metal Yakovlev aircraft was the I-30 or 'Yak-3 of 1941', which more closely resembled the Yak-7. This particular Yak-3 never got beyond the prototype stage because of the very severe shortage of metal for aircraft construction at the time, although some of the design features were incorporated in what was to eventually become the Yak-3. Altogether, 36,737 Yak fighters in this series were built – more than any other Soviet fighter series before or since.

Advanced trainer

Although the Yak-11 had a fighter designation (indicated by the odd number), it was specifically designed as an advanced trainer. Two seats in tandem and a 'low power' Ash-21 seven-cylinder radial engine developing 730 hp were combined with the wings, tail unit and undercarriage of the Yak-3. A very clean, close-fitting engine cowling was fitted and maximum speed was 460 km/h (286 mph). The Yak-11 did not appear until after World War II, but nevertheless, 3,859 were built between 1946 and 1956, some of which were supplied to Communist and Arab air forces. The Yak-11U, with a nosewheel undercarriage, was built in Czechoslovakia.

Although the great majority of Yakovlev's wartime aircraft were fighters, a sizeable number of his pre-war UT-2 trainers and a handful of twin-engined light transports were also built during the war years. The Yak-6 was one of a number of utility aircraft which were designed to be produced from easily-obtained local materials, such as wood, which were simple to build and were powered by Shvetsov's M-11 radial engine, normally used for trainers and sportsplanes. Another example of a utility design to this general specification was Tomashevich's Pegas light *shturmovik* (assault aircraft).

The Yak-6 of 1942 normally had a retractable under-carriage, although it was sometimes left fixed; the engines were sometimes uncowled. Although used mostly for liaison duties when it carried a crew of two and six passengers, the Yak-6 was also used to carry troops behind the lines, as an ambulance or trainer. In addition, it was used for its original purpose of night bomber – NBB, or short-range night bomber, was the alternative designation – when a bomb-load of up to 500 kg (1,100 lb) was carried on external racks.

Another communications aircraft, a four-seat, high-wing, cabin monoplane, rather like the Auster AOP or Piper Cub, was developed from the pre-war AIR-6. Although designed in 1944, the prototype Yak-12 was not completed until 1946. There were several modifications to the basic design and the Yak-12 eventually took over all the roles previously performed by Polikarpov's Po-2. These were military liaison, ambulance and agricultural work, light freight and passenger transport and, infrequently, training. Later versions of the Yak-12 were produced in Poland and China.

First flown in 1946, the Yak-18 was developed from the UT-2 via the 1942 UT-2L which had a long glasshouse canopy over the tandem cockpits and a helmet cowling for the 145 hp M-11D engine. The Yak-18 had a retractable undercarriage and was originally powered by the 160 hp M-11FR which gave it a maximum speed of 249 km/h (154 mph) at sea level. However, in 1957 the type was re-engined with the 260 hp AI-14R nine-cylinder radial engine, becoming the Yak-18A. In the meantime, a version featuring a tricycle undercarriage had been introduced in 1954 as the Yak-18U. This modification had involved moving the main undercarriage legs from the front to the rear wing spar – an exercise which was also carried out on the Yak-11U and Yak-15.

Aerobatic champions

In 1959, Yakovlev produced the Yak-18P, a single-seat variant for the first World Aerobatic Championships held in Bratislava, Czechoslovakia, in 1960. The rear cockpit was covered over, a new fuel system allowing five minutes

Below: the all-metal Yak-9P was built at the end of World War II. The pictured example was captured by United States forces in Korea.
Bottom: a Yak-3 which fought on the Eastern Front with the Normandie-Niemen Regiment is preserved in the Musée de l'Air in Paris

of inverted flight was installed and there was a change in the centre of gravity. The Yak-18P did not win the first year of the Championships, but various modifications of the Yak-18 were built especially for successive World Aerobatic Championships, the Yak-18PM winning in 1966 and again in 1970.

The Yak-18T, a four-seat, low-wing cabin monoplane of 1966 was only remotely related to the Yak-18, although it had the same square-tipped wings and tailplane of the later Yak-18PM and PS. It was designed by A. S. Yakovlev's son, Sergei Aleksandrovich Yakovlev. Originally intended for Aeroflot feeder lines and some other Yak-12 roles, it has developed into a basic trainer for Aeroflot pilots and navigators.

The latest aerobatic Yak, the Yak-50, and its two-seat trainer equivalent the Yak-52, have been developed by a design team under the direction of Sergei Yakovlev from the Yak-18PS and Yak-18A respectively. The principal differences are a slight reduction in overall dimensions and the use of all-metal construction. Both aircraft are powered by the 360 hp M-14P engine; the maximum speed of the Yak-50 is 300 km/h (186 mph) and that of the Yak-52 is 285 km/h (177 mph). Yak-50s came first, second and fifth in the 1976 World Aerobatic Championships.

Flying classrooms
Yakovlev's first postwar 'twins' were not so successful. The Yak-16 light transport of 1947, designed to carry ten to twelve passengers, was unsuitable as a transport, but some were used by the air force as flying classrooms; the Yak-200, designed for this purpose, was abandoned at the prototype stage. Since 1951, dual control conversions of in-service multi-engined aircraft have been used for advanced flying training.

The Yakovlev design bureau produced almost every type of small/medium aircraft up to 1960, including the Yak-14 cargo glider with a payload capacity of 3,500 kg (7,700 lb) in 1948 and three helicopters between 1947 and

1960, when this department was closed down. Apart from postwar military aircraft and the Yak-16, all employed, at least in their original versions, the traditional Yakovlev lightweight mixed construction of wood and tubular metal with fabric and sometimes plywood covering.

The helicopter experiment was not very successful, although it must be remembered that this was in the early days of helicopter development. The department, established in 1944 under Igor Yerlikh, produced its first helicopter in 1947. It was of co-axial layout and made a number of short flights, but suffered from problems associated with oscillation and control. The Yak-100 of 1948 was almost a copy of the Sikorsky S-51 and, although more successful than the first Yakovlev helicopter, early problems were not resolved until the rival Mil Mi-1 was already in production. Finally, the Yak-24 twin-engined helicopter of 1952, with two 1,700 hp ASh-82V engines driving twin tandem rotors, was designed to carry 24 passengers or up to 4,000 kg (8,800 lb) of cargo including light military vehicles. Flutter was again a major problem and, although the Yak-24 was persevered with through

Top: a beautifully-maintained specimen of the Yak-11 trainer. Having force-landed in Cyprus, this aircraft was imported to the United Kingdom for restoration and was appropriately re-registered. Above: developed from the pre-war AIR-6, the Yak-12 was widely used as a club, ambulance, training, agricultural and light transport aircraft

several minor modifications mainly concerned with the rotors and tail, it was finally abandoned.

When, in 1945, it was realised that the Soviet Union lagged behind the other major powers in the development of turbojet-engined aircraft, and the Party Central Committee proposed that the Messerschmitt Me 262 be produced in the USSR, Yakovlev said that he thought this would be a mistake partly because of the aircraft's deficiencies and partly because it would absorb resources which should be used to develop Soviet aircraft. Preliminary work was already in progress on Soviet jet aircraft at several design bureaux including Yakovlev's. The Yakovlev team had decided to build an aircraft which would be as easy to fly as a piston-engined aircraft and determined that the best way of achieving this was to make the engine the only new feature. They therefore adapted the basic Yak-3 airframe to take a single German Jumo 004B axial-flow turbojet. This engine was subsequently built in the Soviet Union as the RD-10 and developed 850 kg (1,875 lb) thrust.

Designated Yak-15, the new fighter used the flying surfaces, rear fuselage and tailwheel undercarriage of the Yak-3U. The forward fuselage was redesigned and parts of the structure strengthened to accommodate the RD-10 in the nose. In addition, the engine exhausted under the centre fuselage, which had to be sheathed in heat-resistant steel; an all-metal roller replaced the normal tailwheel. The first flight of the Yak-15 was carried out by test pilot M. I. Ivanov on 24 April 1946, the same day as the first flight of the MiG-9. Following a brief appearance at the Soviet Aviation Day display in August, both design bureaux received orders for a pre-production batch of aircraft to take part in the October Day fly-past. The first of the 15 Yak-15s was built in only four weeks, the second was completed on 5 October and the last on 21 October, just ten days before the event. However, there was no fly-past because fog grounded all aircraft that day.

The tailwheel undercarriage of the Yak-15 was soon abandoned and with repositioned main legs and a nose-wheel retracting into a blister fairing, the Yak-15 entered Soviet air force service in 1947. It had a maximum speed of 786 km/h (488 mph) at 5,000 m (16,500 ft). The experimental Yak-3R, equipped with an auxiliary rocket engine, had achieved a speed of 820 km/h (510 mph) at 7,800 m (25,590 ft), but was destroyed during tests. A conversion trainer, designated Yak-17UTI, was produced in 1947 with two seats in tandem and a redesigned tail unit. The fighter equivalent, the Yak-17, was powered by a 1,000 kg (2,200 lb) thrust RD-10A and had a maximum speed of 750 km/h (466 mph); this variant was also supplied to Czechoslovakia and Poland.

The Yak-15 and Yak-17, with their moderate performance provided Soviet airmen with some useful jet-age experience; they were, however, in no way comparable with foreign jet fighters. The next Yakovlev fighter, the Yak-23, followed the same general pattern, but was a complete redesign and used more modern design and engineering techniques. As a consequence of the very thin laminar wing section, the undercarriage wheels could no longer be stowed in the wings and were retracted into the fuselage. A 1,590 kg (3,500 lb) thrust Rolls-Royce Derwent 5 engine, imported from the United Kingdom, was used for the prototype which flew in 1947. Production aircraft had a Soviet-built copy of the Derwent, the RD-500. Internal fuel capacity was increased on the Yak-23, and with wing-tip tanks, a more respectable maximum speed was achieved and range was increased from the modest 740 km (460 miles) of the Yak-15 to 1,200 km (745 miles).

While these interim 'pod and boom' types were being produced by the Yakovlev bureau for the Soviet air force, a series of more conventional 'straight-through' fighters was produced experimentally. The first of these, the Yak-19, was completed early in 1947. It had straight flying surfaces but used a thin laminar wing section and the undercarriage retracted into the fuselage.

Also completed in 1947, the Yak-25 had a slightly modified fuselage to accommodate the 1,600 kg (3,525 lb) thrust RD-500 centrifugal-flow engine and all-swept tail

surfaces. Swept-back wings were introduced on the Yak-30 of 1948 which, in all other respects, resembled the Yak-25. Maximum speed was 1,025 km/h (637 mph). The Yak-30 was a contemporary of the MiG-15 and La-15, but was the last of the trio to undergo trials and was not adopted for production. Similarly, the Yak-50 all-weather fighter of 1949, which had a nose radar installation and 'zero-track' main undercarriage units, was not adopted. The Yak-1000 was an experimental transonic delta of 1951 with a very short wingspan.

It was at the beginning of the 1950s that the Yakovlev bureau turned its attention to the first of a series of twin-engined, multi-seat, all-weather fighters which was to prove more successful. The first was the Yak-25–the designation was repeated because the original Yak-25 of 1947 was not adopted by the air force–code-named Flashlight by NATO and was produced in competition with the Mikoyan/Gurevich I-320(R) and Lavochkin La-200. The first flight took place about 1952. The blunt lines of the Yak-25 were a departure from the normally fine aerodynamics of Yakovlev aircraft, despite its all-swept flying surfaces. The crew of two sat behind a vast radar nose which contrasted with the small underslung engine nacelles. Originally powered by two AM-5 turbojets, the majority of Yak-25s were equipped with two AM-9B turbojets which gave a maximum speed in excess of 1,000 km/h (620 mph). Zero-track main undercarriage wheels retracted into the fuselage.

Top: the prototype Yak-18 differed markedly from its successors, which were to dominate the world aerobatic arena in the 1960s. Its helmet cowling and rearwards-retracting tailwheel undercarriage are noteworthy features.
Above: the twin-engined twin-rotor Yak-24 helicopter of 1952 displayed a variety of tail configurations in the development phase. Vehicles could be loaded through the rear fuselage

Yakovlev Yak-28P of the Soviet Air Force

Dimensions
Span 12·95 m (42 ft 6 in)
Length 21·65 m (71 ft 0½ in)

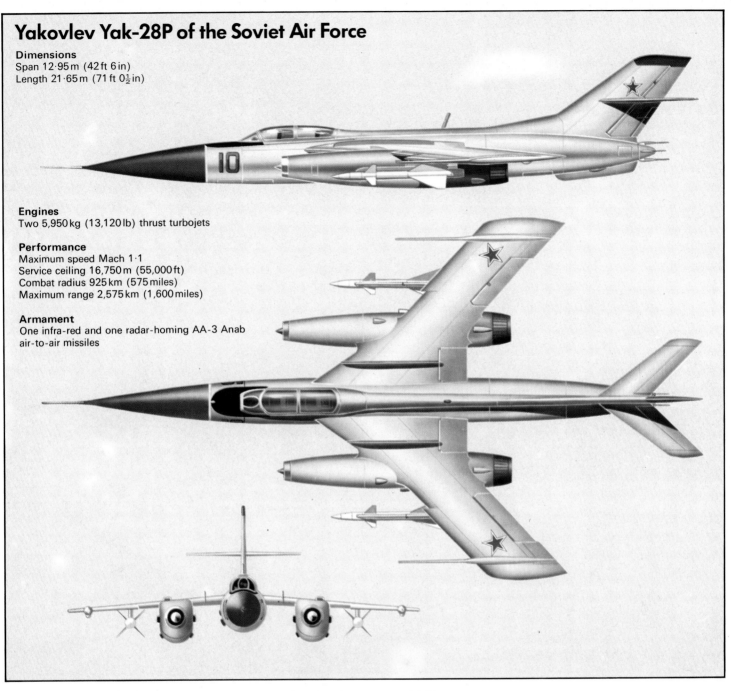

Engines
Two 5,950 kg (13,120 lb) thrust turbojets

Performance
Maximum speed Mach 1·1
Service ceiling 16,750 m (55,000 ft)
Combat radius 925 km (575 miles)
Maximum range 2,575 km (1,600 miles)

Armament
One infra-red and one radar-homing AA-3 Anab
air-to-air missiles

The Yak-25 was produced in two main versions: the all-weather fighter codenamed Flashlight-C and the bombardier nose tactical strike version code-named Flashlight-B. The latter, officially designated Yak-26, had a modified wing, which was further modified by extending and drooping the leading-edge on the final version. The Soviet equivalent of the Lockheed U-2 was a Yak-25 with an unswept high-aspect-ratio wing and R-11 engines. The designation RV was used when it established altitude/payload records in 1959 including an altitude of 20,450 m (67,100 ft) with a 1,000 kg (2,200 lb) payload.

The basic Yak-25 design was aerodynamically refined for the Yak-28, code-named Firebar or Brewer by NATO according to role. The wing was moved from the low-mid-wing position, fuselage and nacelle length were increased considerably and a twin-wheel tandem undercarriage was

The Yak-25 two-seat all-weather interceptor entered service in the mid-1950s with the supersonic MiG-19, each a significant advance in Soviet military aircraft. The Yak-25 led to several important developments, notably the Yak-28

fitted. The engines are reported to be R-11 turbojets with reheat, and maximum speed is estimated at about Mach 1·1. Several versions have been reported, including the basic Yak-28P (Firebar-B) solid-nose all-weather fighter, and Brewer-A, B and C tactical strike aircraft, Brewer-D for photographic reconnaissance. Brewer-E with ECM and the Yak-28U (Maestro) two-seat trainer.

VTOL Freehand

While Sukhoi and Mikoyan experimented with STOL fighters in the mid-1960s, the Yakovlev bureau produced the first Soviet fixed-wing VTOL aircraft (apart from a purely experimental·'flying bedstead' of 1954) which was code-named Freehand by NATO when demonstrated in flight at Domodedovo in 1967. Powered by two turbojets mounted in the forward fuselage, Freehand had a short-span delta wing with clipped wingtips.

The Yak-36 (code-named Forger) is the first Soviet operational fixed-wing VTOL aircraft, and was revealed in 1976 when the aircraft carrier *Kiev* sailed through the Mediterranean to the North Atlantic. The *Kiev*'s aircraft were believed to be from a pre-production batch, as minor variations were noted as well as a two-seat training version. The Yak-36 single-seat strike fighter is powered by a single conventional turbojet and has two lift jets–believed to be designed by P. A. Kolesov–behind the cockpit.

In 1966, the design bureau produced the Yak-40, its first airliner since the unsuccessful Yak-16 of 1948. Yakovlev's chief assistants on the project were Ye. G. Adler, who had helped to design the Yak-15, and Sergei A. Yakovlev. The Yak-40 is a 24-to-32 seat feeder-liner designed to replace the Li-2 (Soviet-built DC-3) and early postwar Soviet transports. The first flight was on 21 October 1966 and the first Aeroflot scheduled service was inaugurated on 30 September 1968. The speed with which it was designed, built and put into regular service was quite remarkable. Only three-and-a-half years after its introduction to Aeroflot routes it was being used on 250 local routes in the USSR. Nearly 1,000 have been built since 1966, of which between 50 and 60 have been exported.

The Yak-40 was designed for regular operation from grass runways with lengths of only 700 m (2,300 ft). The original idea of the third engine was that it should only be used for take-off but in fact it has always been used throughout the flight regime. The engines are AI-25 turbofans, each of which develops 1,500 kg (3,300 lb) thrust. The advertised maximum payload range of the 1973 model was 1,450 km (900 miles) with a payload of 2,720 kg (6,000 lb), but some operators were reported to be disappointed in the aircraft's performance.

Top: a Yak-36 VTOL fighter prepares to land on the Soviet aircraft carrier Kiev. Air for the lift engines is ingested through a dorsal hatch.

Above: the first viable VTOL aircraft flown in the USSR was an experimental design by Yakovlev, code-named Freehand by NATO. Powered by two turbojets, it achieved vertical take-off by combined direct and vectored thrust

*Above: the Yak-40
short-haul airliner entered
Aeroflot service in
September 1968 and by
early 1973 had carried over
eight million passengers. By
mid-1976 over 800 Yak-40s
had been built.
Left: the Yak-42, a much
enlarged and improved
Yak-40, was designed to
utilise three turbofan
power plants*

The Yak-40 has enjoyed one of the biggest sales campaigns for a Soviet aircraft ever carried out in an effort to obtain access to Western and world markets. Sales tours were arranged to cover all five continents and Italian and German certification was received in 1972. However, Italian, German and Greek operators have only used the Yak-40 for short periods before returning their aircraft. The Russians were still negotiating in late 1978 with ICX Aviation Inc for Yak-40 production in the USA. The American built Yak-40 would use American avionics and Garrett TFE 731-3 engines on commuter models. Should the deal be completed, Soviet production would be terminated and the tooling would be shipped to the USA.

The Yak-42 is a much-enlarged version of the Yak-40 with a take-off weight of 52,000 kg (114,640 lb) designed to carry up to 120 passengers. Range is 1,000 km (620 miles) with maximum payload of 14,500 kg (32,000 lb). By today's standards the Yak-42 is still able to fulfil Yakovlev's ideal of simplicity. Prototypes were tested with different moderately-swept wings: the first prototype had 11 degrees of sweepback and the second had 23 degrees of wing sweep, the second version being chosen for production. The three Lotarev D-36 engines were designed to minimise noise and fuel consumption; the aircraft itself was designed to conform to US Federal Aviation regulations and was first flown on 7 March 1975.

Alexander Yakovlev has been one of the leading Soviet designers for over 40 years and, unlike many of his contemporaries, has escaped any form of detention. In the 44 years from 1933 to 1977, since the first Yakovlev aircraft was mass-produced, over 66,000 Yaks of all types have been produced by Soviet factories.

FIRST THROUGH THE BARRIER

Chuck Yeager's supersonic flight on 14 October 1947 heralded a new era in aviation

Among the notable 'firsts' in aviation history is the occasion when a manned aircraft exceeded the speed of sound in level flight. The date was 14 October 1947, the machine was the Bell XS-1, and the pilot, Captain Charles 'Chuck' Yeager, became famed as 'the first man to break the sound barrier'. Although 'Chuck' Yeager is assured a place in history as the first man to exceed the speed of sound, his wartime service was also highly creditable.

At 18 he enlisted in the US Army Air Force, became an aircraft mechanic and was a crew chief on North American AT-6 trainers when the United States entered World War II. The following year he was selected for pilot training and graduated in March 1943 with the rank of flight officer. He was then assigned to the newly-formed 363rd Fighter Squadron of the 357th Fighter Group to fly Bell P-39 Airacobras. His coolness and capability in an emergency were twice exhibited while flying the P-39. On one occasion undercarriage failure necessitated a belly-landing and, when another aircraft suddenly burst into flames, Yeager had to bale out.

Ace in a day

In November 1943 the Group moved to England where it was equipped with the new North American P-51B Mustang long-range escort fighter, becoming the first unit in the Eighth Air Force to use the type. On Yeager's seventh combat operation, an escort to Berlin, he claimed a Messerschmitt Bf 109 destroyed, but two days later his Mustang was shot down by enemy fighters over south-east France and he had to take to his parachute. Fortunately he was befriended by members of the French Resistance for, wounded in both feet during the air fight, he might otherwise have been captured while seeking medical attention. Eventually he was fit enough to make his way to the Spanish border with another American airman. Spotted by border guards, they were fired on and Yeager's companion was wounded, but they were successful in reaching neutral territory. After a short period of internment, Yeager reached Gibraltar and was flown back to England in July to rejoin his unit, which was then based at Leiston, Suffolk.

Once an airman had been returned via the French escape network it was policy not to let him resume combat in the European Theatre of Operations, lest he be shot down again and unwittingly divulge details of his first escape under enemy interrogation. As the Allied cross-Channel invasion had been successful and the liberation of France seemed imminent, the restrictions were soon no longer necessary. Until official approval was forthcoming, however, Yeager was confined to local flights, but it was rumoured that during this period the frustrated pilot chanced upon an enemy bomber over the North Sea and promptly dispatched it. Finally back on authorised combat missions, Yeager, flying his personal Mustang nicknamed *Glamorous Glennis*, wasted no time in displaying his prowess as a fighter pilot. As leader of a 357th Group formation on an escort to Bremen on 12 October 1944, he attacked a formation of Bf 109s and destroyed five to

Charles Yeager (left), the first pilot to break the sound barrier, with Peter Twiss, the Briton who set a world speed record of twice the speed of sound in 1956. However, Yeager had set an unofficial record of Mach 2·5 three years before Twiss's flight

earn the unusual accolade of 'ace in a day'. Early in November Yeager shot down a Messerschmitt Me 262 jet which he caught on its landing approach and, on the 27th of the month, added four Focke Wulf Fw 190s to his score during a vast air battle near Magdeburg. By February 1945 he had been credited with 13½ enemy aircraft in 64 missions and was returned to the United States.

Leading test pilot

In the summer of 1945 his flying and technical expertise gained him a post with the Fighter Test Branch at Wright Field, the American equivalent of RAE Farnborough. Here he worked on development programmes for the Lockheed P-80 and Republic P-84 jets and also evaluated several captured German and Japanese fighter aircraft. Graduating from the Test Pilot School at this base, he was posted to the experimental test airfield at Muroc, California, where he remained until September 1954 and established himself as the USAF's leading test pilot.

During World War II many pilots flying high-performance aircraft had encountered the phenomenon known as compressibility. Severe vibration and loss of control had occurred and, in some cases, aircraft had disintegrated. Evidence collected from pilots who experienced compressibility forces in high-speed dives led many authorities to believe that the shock waves built up by an aircraft reaching the speed of sound – approximately 1,223 km/h (760 mph) at sea level – would inevitably cause it to become uncontrollable and break up.

The USAAF began research into compressibility in 1944 and gave Bell Aircraft a contract to build a special aircraft which could be used to investigate flight at supersonic speeds. The design featured a bullet-shaped fuselage with four rocket motors to obtain the necessary power for the desired high speeds. The wing and tail were given very narrow sections but the whole structure was extremely strong. As the rocket motors consumed the total fuel supply in two-and-a-half minutes, the XS-1 (later redesignated X-1) was designed to be taken aloft by a Boeing B-29 Superfortress and launched for its speed runs, afterwards gliding back to base when its rocket fuel had been exhausted.

By the time the USAF was ready to attempt supersonic flight with the XS-1, the death of test pilot Geoffrey de Havilland and other fatal incidents had strengthened the belief that supersonic flight was extremely hazardous. Volunteers were asked for from the small band of military test pilots and Captain Charles Yeager was one of those selected to carry out the XS-1 programme. Small in stature and an accomplished test pilot noted for his skill and stability in difficult situations, Yeager was considered highly suitable for this exploration of the unknown. He was in no doubt as to the dangerous nature of his mission when, on 14 October 1947, he took off in the B-29 launch aircraft for the first attempt to push the XS-1 (serial number 46-62) through the sonic barrier. The aircraft's first powered flight had occurred in December 1946.

Yeager flew with the 357th Fighter Group, the first Eighth Air Force group to be equipped with the North American P-51 Mustang long-range escort fighter. Three P-51Ds and a P-51B of the Eighth Air Force are illustrated. Yeager scored all but one of his 13½ victories in a four-month period

Speed of sound

The test was to be conducted over the USAF experimental station at Muroc dry lake, California. At 2,130 m (7,000 ft) Yeager climbed out of the B-29's bomb-bay and entered the XS-1 suspended below. It was necessary to climb down a ladder and squeeze through a small hatch into the cramped cockpit while being assailed by the blast of the slipstream through the open bomb-bay. To add to his discomfort Yeager had a couple of badly-bruised ribs, the result of being thrown from a horse the previous evening. Settled in the XS-1 and wearing only standard Air Force flying garb with leather helmet, Yeager started cockpit checks while the B-29 climbed to an altitude of 8,000 m (26,000 ft). With all systems clear, the Superfortress dived to increase speed to 400 km/h (250 mph).

Yeager dropped away, fired the rocket motors and 2,700 kg (6,000 lb) of thrust sent the small craft soaring into the stratosphere. Little sound from the rocket motors reached the cockpit and Yeager later remarked that, although the Mach instrumentation showed he was exceeding the speed of sound, there was no sensation of speed. He felt disappointed that there was no other indication of the advance from subsonic to sonic flight. Before the rocket fuel was exhausted the XS-1 had flown at Mach 1·05. A seven-and-a-half minute glide followed and Yeager brought XS-1 in for a safe 257 km/h (160 mph) touch-down at Muroc. The feat was not made public until eight months later, by which time many other sonic

flights had been performed with the Bell proving that, with a strong, well-streamlined airframe, the sonic barrier was no real obstacle to advancing aircraft speeds.

Yeager's work was principally with high-performance aircraft and in 1953 he flew to Okinawa, Japan to evaluate a MiG-15 presented to the USAF by a defecting North Korean. Sonic speed research was still a priority and Yeager made over 40 flights in the Bell research aircraft, exceeding 1,600 km/h (1,000 mph) and reaching 21,000 m (70,000 ft). On 12 December 1953, flying the Bell X-1A he set a speed record of 2,650 km/h (1,650 mph).

In 1954 Major Yeager returned to service with operational units, and in October was given command of the 417th Fighter Squadron in Germany. Further squadron commands followed his return to the United States and three years later, in June 1961, he was back in test work, although chiefly in an administrative capacity. In July 1966 he took command of the 405th Fighter Wing in South East Asia and flew 127 operations in North American F-100 Super Sabres. Later appointments included that of Vice-Commander of the Seventeenth Air Force in Germany during the early 1970s. On his retirement from the USAF in March 1975, as a Brigadier-General, 'Chuck' Yeager had flown over 10,000 hours in 155 different types of aircraft. As a mark of national appreciation, in December 1976 President Ford presented the retired general with a specially-struck silver medal to honour his accomplishments in the realms of high-speed flight.

Yeager is pictured with his wife in a Bell 47 helicopter. Yeager's flying skills, technical knowledge and even temperament made him a natural test-pilot. Between 1945 and 1954 he made notable contributions to aviation, not only with supersonic flights, but also on the test programmes of the Lockheed P-80 and Republic P-84 jets

Yokosuka

The products of Japan's First Naval Air Arsenal ranged from training biplanes to the Ohka suicide bomb

In June 1912 the Imperial Japanese Navy established the Naval Aeronautical Research Committee and a naval air station was set up on the Oppama coast near Yokosuka. Following the purchase of several American and European aircraft, modified seaplane versions of these foreign types were built and tested. Two designers working at the First Naval Air Technical Arsenal in Yokosuka were lieutenants Magoshi and Nakajima and in 1916 the float biplane Type Yokosho (short for Yokosuka) was schemed. The Type Yokosho was the first aircraft of Japanese design and went into production at the Yokosuka Arsenal in 1917. A total of 218 aircraft designated Ro-Ko and powered by 200 hp Hispano-Suiza engines was built at Yokosuka and in Aichi and Nakajima factories. Magoshi's Yi-Ko trainer seaplane followed, 70 being built. From then on Yokosuka played a leading part in producing navy designs. The E1Y1 emerged victorious from a 1923 design competition and went into service as the Navy Type 14 Sea Reconnaissance biplane, 320 being built, 23 of these at Yokosuka. Then came the K1Y1 Type 13 trainer seaplane, six of the 104 built by 1925 being constructed at the Arsenal workshops.

Above: the B4Y1 Carrier Attacker served with success in the war with China in 1937-38, but had become obsolete by 1941. Right: some 5,770 examples of the K5Y Intermediate Trainer were produced between 1934 and 1945 in both landplane and floatplane versions. Below: developed from the British Avro 504, the K2Y Primary Trainer flew with the Japanese navy from 1928 onwards

Submarine-borne scout

The Type 3 Trainer was none other than a modified Avro 504 biplane and a total of 360 was delivered to the navy between 1928 and 1940. K2Y1 was powered by a licence-built 130 hp British Mongoose engine and K2Y2 by a Japanese 130 hp Kamikaze. The three-seat K5Y1 twin-float long-range reconnaissance biplane proved unsuccessful, only 17 being completed. In contrast, the K4Y1 float trainer displayed excellent flying qualities and 211 were built, designated Type 90 and powered by a 160 hp Kamikaze engine. Their longevity was remarkable and a number were released after years of service for civil use. A diminutive single-seat reconnaissance float biplane for submarine use, capable of being dismantled in record time for storage in a hangar on the submarine's deck, was developed into the E6Y1 or Type 91. Tested by Lt Cdr Jiro

Saba aboard submarine I-51 in 1931, the prototype was followed by nine production machines.

An intermediate training biplane, built and tested in 1931, was developed into the K5Y with the aid of engineers from the Kawanishi firm. The new prototype, test-flown in December 1933, was a single-bay staggered unequal-span biplane of mixed construction with pupil and instructor in tandem open cockpits. Power was provided

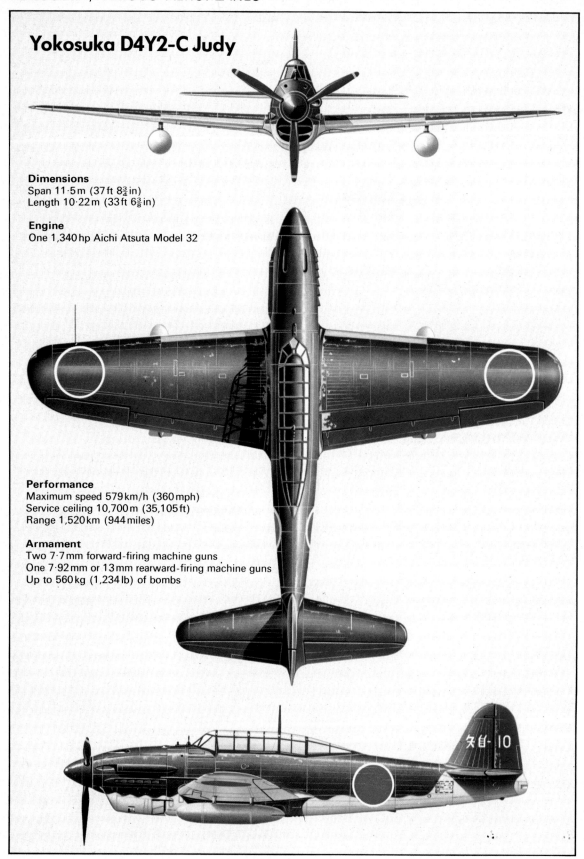

Yokosuka D4Y2-C Judy

Dimensions
Span 11·5 m (37 ft 8¾ in)
Length 10·22 m (33 ft 6⅜ in)

Engine
One 1,340 hp Aichi Atsuta Model 32

Performance
Maximum speed 579 km/h (360 mph)
Service ceiling 10,700 m (35,105 ft)
Range 1,520 km (944 miles)

Armament
Two 7·7 mm forward-firing machine guns
One 7·92 mm or 13 mm rearward-firing machine guns
Up to 560 kg (1,234 lb) of bombs

Above: the MXY-7 Ohka was produced for Kamikaze attacks on US warships. Carried to the target zone by a Mitsubishi G4M Betty bomber, three rockets propelled it after launching. Of 74 dispatched, no more than four are known to have hit their intended targets. Right: only 20 H5Y1 flying boats entered Japanese navy service. Below: the E14Y1 was a submarine-borne reconnaissance seaplane which made the sole wartime bombing raid on the United States

by a 340 hp Hitachi Amakaze radial engine with a Townend ring. Designated Type 93 Intermediate Trainer, initial production was by the Kawanishi company. It was most successful and was manufactured by Yokosuka and no fewer than seven private aircraft firms. A total of 5,770 had been completed when production ceased in 1945. Most were K5Y1 landplanes, but the total included a considerable number of K5Y2 and K5Y3 twin-float versions for operation from water.

Several new carrier torpedo bomber prototypes were rejected in 1932 and the Yokosuka 'fall-back' design, the B3Y1, was adopted as the Type 92 Carrier Attacker. The 130 built, with 600 hp Type 91 inline engines, proved ineffective and little better than their elderly predecessors, the Mitsubishi Type 89 biplanes. Success over China in the mid-1930s was minimal and they were soon withdrawn. A 1934 competition for a replacement resulted in success for a new Yokosuka design, the B4Y1 or Type 96 Carrier

Attacker single-bay biplane. Five Yokosho-built prototypes were followed by 200 series machines, produced by Mitsubishi, Nakajima and the Hiro Arsenal. Powered by a 840 hp Nakajima Hikari radial engine in a close-fitting cowling and with a fixed, spatted undercarriage, the three-seat B4Y1 reached a maximum 278 km/h (173 mph), had a range of 1,574 km (978 miles) and carried an 800 kg torpedo or 500 kg (1,100 lb) of bombs. Type 96s fought in the war against China during 1937–38, but by the time of the attack on Pearl Harbour only one first-line unit, aboard the carrier *Hosho*, was equipped with B4Y1s. Coded Jean by the Allies they were not encountered after December 1941 when American operations began in earnest.

A competition for the E9W1 submarine-borne seaplane, which had succeeded the E6Y1, was held and resulted in the Yokosho E14Y1 seaplane, which was tested and placed in production, 125 being built by Watanabe up to

1943. A two-seat, twin-float, cantilever low-wing monoplane, with an enclosed crew canopy and powered by a 340 hp Hitachi Tempu radial, the E14Y1 reached 246 km/h (153 mph) at sea level. Its most famous exploit was the only bombing raid on the United States in World War II. Warrant Officer Fujita, alone in an E14Y1 from submarine I-25 dropped four 76 kg bombs on the Oregon coastal area. Designated Type O Small Reconnaissance seaplane by the navy, it was known as Glenn to Allied Intelligence.

During the early 1930s Arsenal and Nakajima engineers produced three successive biplane dive bomber prototypes, but they were all unsuccessful. The H5Y1 or Type 99 flying boat (Allied code-name Cherry) had a parasol wing and two 1,200 hp radial engines, but when 20 finally went into service in 1940 they were already obsolete. The H7Y1, with four Jumo 205 diesel engines, was intended for long-range reconnaissance over Hawaii from bases in Micronesia. A single 1939 prototype had a lightweight structure to achieve a range of 9,250 km (5,750 miles) and consequently it lacked stability and suffered severe vibrations; the project was cancelled.

The First Naval Air Technical Arsenal's complementary role to the Japanese private aircraft industry in supplying the whole range of the Imperial navy's needs was obvious, but two later designs showed a high level of technical ability, equal to the best in Japan. First was the D4Y1 Suisei (Comet), developed from the Heinkel He 118V4 dive bomber prototype imported and tested in 1938. A Yokosho team led by Masao Yamana developed

a smaller, mid-wing, all-metal, two-seat dive bomber with extremely clean lines and featuring an internal bomb-bay for a single bomb of up to 500 kg. The first prototype flew in December 1940; four more prototypes and 660 production aircraft followed. Wing flutter problems precluded dive bombing and early series aircraft, powered by Aichi Atsuta 1,200 hp water-cooled engines, were adapted for reconnaissance as D4Y1-Cs. With a maximum speed of 552 km/h (343 mph) at 4,750 m (15,585 ft), they operated effectively from carriers and land bases from late 1942. With strengthened wings, D4Y1s were accepted for dive bombing duties in March 1943, production continuing through the improved D4Y2 and the radial-engined D4Y3 and D4Y4 to reach an overall total of 2,038. All versions were coded Judy by the Allies.

The second impressive Yokosho design was P1Y Ginga (Milky Way) developed by Yamana and Tadanao Mitsuzi. It was a mid-wing, all-metal medium bomber with contours even more aesthetically pleasing than those of D4Y. Powered by twin 1,820 hp Nakajima Homare 11 radials, Ginga flew for the first time in mid-1943. It had a crew of three, defensive armament of two flexibly-mounted 20 mm Type 99 cannon, one in the glazed nose and the second at the rear of the short, streamlined crew canopy. An 800 kg torpedo or 1,000 kg (2,200 lb) of bombs could be carried.

Development problems were immense and difficulties with the Homare engines were never resolved. The 1,098 examples of the Ginga and its night fighter version the Kyokko (Aurora) armed with four obliquely-mounted 20 mm cannon played an active role only in the last six months of World War II, many being expended in what were virtually suicide missions. Known as Frances to the Allies, it had a top speed of 547 km/h (340 mph).

Other Yokosho designs which did not pass the experimental stage were the D3Y Myojo (Venus) wood structure trainer developed from the D3A dive bomber and the very advanced Y-40 project R2Y Keiun (Beautiful Cloud) high-speed, land-based reconnaissance aircraft with tricycle undercarriage and twin coupled 1,700 hp Atsuta 30 engines driving a six-bladed propeller. The one prototype accomplished a single test flight before destruction in a bombing raid.

Yokosuka also produced the MX series of navy special-purpose aircraft, research aircraft, radio-controlled target drones and gliders, the latter including the MXY-5 transport of which 12 were built, and finally decoy replicas of the P1Y1 and G4M2 bombers. The one well-known design in this special-purpose series was the MXY-7, named Ohka (Cherry Blossom), but known as Baka, or 'foolish' to the Allies. It was a single-seat suicide aircraft powered by three Type 4 Model 20 rockets with a total thrust of 800 kg (1,760 lb). After tests as gliders series production started and 852 were built. The nose warhead usually weighed 1,200 kg (2,646 lb). The Ohka first went into operation on 21 March 1945, suspended in the open bomb-bay of specially-modified Mitsubishi Betty bombers. Despite sinking some American ships, many Ohka aircraft were lost when their mother aircraft were shot down. Ohka 22, a smaller version of the original Ohka 11 for use with the faster P1Y1 bomber, was in production at the time of the Japanese surrender in 1945. The torpedo-shaped Ohka had a small raised canopy over the pilot's cockpit and twin fins and rudders. It spanned just 5 m (16 ft) and reached a maximum speed of 649 km/h (403 mph) at 3,500 m (11,480 ft). However, with the arrival of the American forces of occupation in August 1945, aircraft production at the Yokosuka Arsenal was discontinued.

Storm over Suez

The Yom Kippur War brought Israel once more into conflict with her Arab neighbours

Unlike the Six Day War of June 1967, the Yom Kippur War of October 1973 found Israel unprepared. Under pressure from the United States which was responsible for the supply of the majority of her military equipment, Israel was unwilling to appear as the aggressor in the eyes of the world. In addition, Israeli and world attention had been momentarily diverted to the Palestinian attack on Soviet emigrants in Austria at just the moment that the Arab ground forces were being assembled for the attacks across the Suez Canal and against the Golan Heights on the Syrian border.

The Yom Kippur War presented another vital difference which the Arab world was determined to exploit–that it was fighting, not as an aggressor but as liberator of Arab territories, unreasonably occupied by Israel for seven

Above and below: the Israeli air force's ability to make the maximum use of its existing equipment is typified by its use of the Potez CM170 Magister trainer in the light attack role. Flown by reserve pilots, Magisters proved effective in attacks on vehicles and fortified positions using bombs, rockets and machine gun fire. A prodigious array of stores is illustrated

years. There had, moreover, occurred a growing tally of incidents in which Israeli forces had provoked Arab units into combat, and often to their destruction; the latest such event had occurred on 13 September when eight Syrian jet fighters had been shot down at Latakia.

Obsolescent equipment

Although no one could be blind to the efficiency and sophistication of the Israeli forces, the Arab governments obviously felt that their own continuous heavy build-up of Russian-supplied equipment of apparently modern concept would provide parity in quality and superiority in numbers. Indeed the Egyptian and Syrian air forces together fielded almost 1,000 fighters, fighter-bombers, bombers, transports and helicopters, including 260 MiG-21s and 175 Sukhoi Su-7s. Against them were ranged fewer than 500 Israeli first-line aircraft, of which 150 were McDonnell Douglas A-4 Skyhawks and 140 McDonnell Douglas F-4 Phantoms. Clearly the Arabs grossly over-rated the MiG-21 which, though an efficient point-defence interceptor, carried a puny punch as a ground-support fighter-bomber. On the other hand, the F-4 Phantom–unquestionably the world's most accomplished and versatile fighter at the time–could lift up to 7,260 kg (16,000 lb) of sophisticated ordnance. This weight was four times the load of an Su-7, seven times that of the MiG-21, and more than ten times that of the principal Arab close-support fighter, the ancient MiG-17.

Both sides were guilty of making exaggerated claims but, had Israeli claims been substantiated by fact, the Arab air forces would have ceased to exist long before the end of the 19-day conflict, while according to broadcast losses the Heyl Ha'Avir or Israeli Air Force (IAF) seemed capable of fighting for ever.

Independent intelligence

The Americans, in whose interests an Israeli victory lay and who were concerned to witness the efficacy of their equipment in combat, maintained reconnaissance cover at extreme altitude with Lockheed SR-71A aircraft during the war and achieved more realistic and less prejudiced intelligence results than either of the warring opponents. Their figures for the losses suffered were put at 242 Egyptian, 179 Syrian and 21 Iraqi aircraft, compared with 114 Israeli aircraft lost. At any rate, they regarded the Israeli losses sufficiently worrying to mount an impressive airlift of replacement arms and new electronic countermeasures (ECM) equipment. American-supplied reinforcements included at least 48 F-4s and about 80 A-4s. While Eastern Bloc nations did attempt some reinforcement of the Arab forces, President Sadat, in eventually accepting cease-fire terms, complained that he could no longer fight Israel and America at the same time.

Although the war was fought simultaneously by Syria on Israel's northern border and by Egypt across the Suez Canal, it was the latter campaign that featured the bitterest fighting, the most air activity and, eventually, proved the key to the war's conclusion. The Latakia incident provoked Syria's President Assad to conspire with President Sadat to commence preparations for a co-ordinated surprise attack on Israel. The chosen day for the assault was 6 October, the Day of Atonement–Yom Kippur–for the Israelis. While the latter lived in a false sense of security dating from their victorious Six Day War, the Egyptians planned their assault across the Suez Canal on the formidable Bar Lev fortifications lining the eastern bank with secrecy and ingenuity; the aim of the Arab nations was to rid Sinai and the Golan Heights of the Israeli forces of occupation.

Element of surprise

On Friday, 5 October, as massed Egyptian forces were spotted moving up to the Suez Canal, the Israelis suddenly recognised their danger and frantically ordered their forces on to the alert. At 1400 hours in the afternoon of the following day, 1,000 Egyptian guns thundered a barrage as the infantry quickly crossed the canal at four points under its cover. The previous night Egyptian commandos had secretly crossed to the eastern bank and

Above: a Sukhoi Su-7 of the Egyptian air force in combat with an Israeli Dassault Mirage III. Su-7 ground attack fighters were extensively used by the Arab air forces in the Yom Kippur War and suffered heavy losses. They were especially vulnerable to groundfire and far less manoeuvrable than the smaller and faster Mirage interceptors, which almost invariably emerged victors

sealed the Israeli flame-discharger nozzles with liquid cement, rendering them impotent.

The Egyptians held the initiative from the outset in the air as they did on the ground, depending for the defence of the west bank upon an impressive belt of surface-to-air missiles (SAMs) and radar-controlled 23 mm flak, and throwing forward their ground-support aircraft against such targets as Bir Gifgâfa, the main Israeli command base in Sinai, and el Tasa, the forward Bar Lev brigade headquarters. Such was the confusion created by the Egyptian *blitz* tactics that the IAF did not respond for two hours, by which time Egyptian forces were crossing the canal in considerable strength.

Losses on this first day were estimated at 11 Israeli aircraft, mostly shot down by SAMs and flak, and ten

Egyptian aircraft, of which about seven were downed by Phantoms and three by Hawk missiles defending Bir Gifgâfa. The Egyptians also attempted to bomb Tel Aviv with Tupolev Tu-16s, launching a Kelt stand-off bomb which was shot down by an IAF Phantom. By the evening of this first day, on which 200 Egyptian aircraft were thrown into the battle, the attacking armies had penetrated the Bar Lev line and their tanks were fanning out across Sinai.

Sunday, 7 October witnessed some of the heaviest fighting of the whole war on the ground, at sea and in the air. Stung by the weight of Egyptian air attacks on the previous day, the IAF now countered with attacks on the SAM sites and enemy airfields, losing about six A-4s in doing so. However, little damage was caused to Egypt's well-dispersed and concrete-protected air bases, as much had been learned from the devastating pre-emptive Israeli air strikes in the opening hours of the Six Day War. While Egyptian helicopters brought assault forces into the Sinai combat areas, 36 MiG-17s and Su-7s were lost to the defences during attacks on Israeli air bases.

Extravagant claims

The following day it was the Egyptians' turn to attempt to destroy the Israeli ground-to-air missile sites, striking installations at Baluza, Judi and Samarah, and bases at

Bir Thamada, Mulayhis, Umm Khisheib and Umm Marjam in Sinai. Both sides made extravagant claims of aircraft destroyed but it seems that about 15 Israeli A-4s, F-4s and Dassault Mirages were shot down, mostly by groundfire, in addition to about four helicopters destroyed on the ground at Bir Thamada. Egyptian losses were said to be roughly the same, seven MiG-17s having fallen to Raytheon Hawk missiles.

While the Israeli ground forces suffered a major defeat in Sinai on the 9th, with the destruction of the 190th Tank Brigade, their A-4s and F-4s made vain attempts to attack the Nile Delta airfields at Mansurah and Qadmiyah, but were frustrated by the Egyptian missile defences which evidently destroyed about 16 of the attackers. By now Egypt, Syria and Israel were seeking to support their victory claims by displaying captured enemy pilots.

On Wednesday the 10th the Israeli Air Force continued to attack the Egyptian missile screen which was now being deepened as a belt of SAMs was established on the east bank of the Suez Canal. These attacks, and others on forward airfields and the bridges over the canal met with only limited success and were accompanied by the loss of about a dozen IAF aircraft, including four helicopters. The Israelis had by now checked the Egyptian advance into Sinai and were content for the time being to hold a line some 19–24 km (12–15 miles) east of the canal.

Left: the Israeli Chief of Staff, Lt Gen David Elazar, watches the progress of the battle over the Suez Canal from a helicopter on 19 October 1973. By this stage of the war Israel had lost over a hundred warplanes in combat

American airlift

By 12 October independent observers estimated that Egypt had thus far suffered the loss of 82 fighters and fighter-bombers, plus 17 helicopters, and the Syrians 80 fighters and fighter-bombers, plus seven helicopters, a total of 186 aircraft. The same sources estimated IAF losses at 94 aircraft, including sixteen helicopters. The following day Israel made an extraordinary revelation– that the nation possessed war material for no more than four further days of warfare. Whether or not this was just one more ploy in Israel's campaign to win American succour, it certainly had the desired effect when the Americans decided to commence airlifting huge quantities of replacement equipment, as well as highly-sophisticated ECM items. Numerous IAF jet aircraft were by now being repaired at home factories, having suffered serious damage from heat-seeking SA-7 Strella missiles, and US counter-measures equipment was provided to lend immunity from these weapons.

Day Nine, 14 October, was a critical point in the battle for Sinai. Egyptian armoured units made strenuous attempts to force the passes of Khatmia and Mitla, but encountered such determined opposition that a major tank battle developed, which cost Egypt the loss of at least one hundred tanks, and Israel almost as many. More important, it prompted Egypt to rush large numbers of

Above: the MiG-17 shared ground attack duties with the Su-7 in the Egyptian and Syrian air forces, both air arms having over 100 MiG-17s on strength at the outbreak of hostilities.
Left: according to Israeli sources, Arab air losses totalled 248 Egyptian and 221 Syrian aircraft between 6 and 24 October. A MiG-17 is illustrated

tanks across the canal which it had been holding back in readiness for an anticipated Israeli airborne assault on the west bank.

The significance of Egypt's denuding her west bank reserves was felt two days later when an Israeli column not only battered its way to the canal in the south, but in the dead of night managed to send some tanks across to the west bank. Within hours, before the Egyptian air force reacted to this threat, a small but well-defined bridgehead had been established. From this point on, despite tremendous losses, the initiative on the Sinai front passed almost exclusively to the Israelis who, the following day received 24 replacement F-4s and a large number of Shrike air-to-ground radar-homing missiles from America.

Israeli bridgehead

On 18 October, the Israeli west bank pocket was consolidated with the construction of a bridge over the canal. At last the Egyptians woke to the real danger of the bridgehead and attempted to destroy it. The Israelis had, however, overrun the SAM sites in the immediate vicinity and were able to give effective air cover to their troops so that, when Egyptian Su-7s attempted to attack the bridgehead under MiG-21 top cover, vicious air battles developed with IAF Phantoms and Mirages, from which the Egyptians certainly emerged second best.

The next four days brought catastrophe to the Egyptians, with the Israelis on a veritable rampage west of the canal. On the 19th, the Egyptians lost about 20 aircraft, the next day a further ten, followed by about 15 on the 21st. By the evening of the 22nd, Israeli forces controlled the Egyptian airfields at Fayid, Kabrit and Kasfareet, and were threatening the important air base at Abu Sueir. Large numbers of Egyptian SAMs had been destroyed or captured so that the much-vaunted missile screen was no longer able to protect the rear areas.

The inevitable cease-fire, agreed by President Sadat, whose Third Army faced encirclement and annihilation by sophisticated American weaponry should have come into effect of 22 October. However, fighting, in the air and on the ground, flared up time and again for a further two days.

The Syrian Front
In the north the pattern of the war ran much the same as in the south, with initial success attending Syrian forces in their assault on the Israeli-occupied Golan Heights, and Mount Hermon fell to helicopter-borne assault troops on the first day. However, the Syrians failed to move their SAMs forward quickly enough to protect their ground forces from heavy air attacks by IAF Skyhawks.

As in the south, the Israelis now recognised the importance of the Syrian SAM screen, and set about an all-out attempt to destroy the sites and missile vehicles. During the first five days, air losses on both sides mounted quickly, though it was noticeable that most IAF losses were incurred over the ground battle area, suggesting that Syria's rear areas were less well protected by SAMs. A number of crippling strikes against targets at Damascus, Homs, Latakia, Minat al Bayda, Qatinah and Tartus were achieved by the IAF with little loss.

Despite the severity of the fighting in Sinai, and the obvious difficulty experienced by Israel in fighting on two fronts, it was in the north that Israel first made significant headway against the Arabs on the ground. On 11 October, the Syrians began a withdrawal from the Golan Heights (though Syrian and Moroccan troops held firm on Mount Hermon), the reason for this evidently being the enforced withdrawal of Syrian air cover (both missiles and fighters) from the battlefield to give protection to the towns and factories in the rear as well as airfields.

By 16 October, the Israelis had come up against the Saasa defence line and were checked. Five days later they attempted to assault Mount Hermon using about 200 helicopter-borne troops and some 80 paratroops. The battle on and over this key point continued up to and beyond the so-called cease-fire, as both sides threw in airborne troops under cover provided by their respective air forces.

On the last day of fighting, in a show of strength and backed by the newly-delivered American ECM equipment, the IAF launched a number of 'strategic' raids against Syria's industrial plants, including a devastating raid by 60 aircraft – many of them bomb-carrying Phantoms – on a large Damascus oil installation. About ten aircraft were lost by each side.

Seven years earlier, Israel won the Six Day War by use of pre-emptive surprise and superior air power. To guard against a repetition, the Arab nations had acquired large quantities of SAMs from Russia, while their air forces –

almost totally destroyed in 1967 – were rebuilt from scratch. Nevertheless, both Egypt and Syria failed to acquire really modern aircraft and the combat aircraft were still much the same as in the previous war. Moreover, as before, the Arabs again fielded a roughly two-to-one numerical superiority. By adopting the Israeli surprise and *blitz* tactics at the outset, the Arabs certainly looked set to achieve their aims quickly, and there is no doubt that after about five days of catastrophic setbacks the Israelis' situation seemed desperate.

The key to the air war, and therefore almost certainly to the final outcome of the whole conflict, was undoubtedly the Arabs' missile network. The brilliant plans followed by the IAF to attack the missile sites, irrespective of losses, certainly prevented their effective use in defence of the ground forces. Although the SAM network was never totally destroyed, it was rendered almost impotent by the arrival of American countermeasures equipment. Perhaps it is significant that while the United States was prepared to release quantities of very modern aircraft and equipment to safeguard Israel's survival, the Soviet Union was evidently reluctant (or unable) to supply to the Arab nations similar *matériel*.

Below: Egyptian surface-to-air and anti-tank missiles made important contributions to that country's early successes against Israeli forces. AT-1 Snapper anti-tank missiles are pictured. Bottom: high level attack was guarded against by Egyptian SA-2 Guideline missiles, a captured example of which is being recovered for Israeli evaluation and testing

Taming the Thunderbolt

Hubert Zemke was responsible for the successful introduction to service of the Republic P-47

Often acclaimed as the most talented and successful American fighter leader of World War II, Hubert Zemke was well-deserving of such praise. His principal achievement was developing tactics with the Republic P-47 Thunderbolt and using them with deadly effect against the Luftwaffe interceptors which rose to meet the American daylight bombers raiding German targets. Zemke's P-47 group, the 56th, showed what could be done with the heavy fighter and set a score of enemy aircraft destroyed which was unsurpassed by any other American fighter unit operating from the United Kingdom.

The son of Swiss emigrants, Hubert Zemke was born in 1914 at Missoula, Montana where his father had a sheep ranch. Hubert attended university where he coupled academic promise with success in sports—notably football and boxing. Attracted to aviation he enlisted in the US Army and eventually gained his wings in the Air Corps. A natural aptitude for the mechanical earned him the position of assistant engineering officer with the 8th Fighter Group at Langley Field, Virginia, and selection for a variety of special assignments.

This appreciation of technical matters led to a posting to the United Kingdom in 1941 where he studied British fighter equipment and tactics and advised the Royal Air Force on the use of the Curtiss P-40 Tomahawk, then arriving from the United States. When the RAF decided the Tomahawk was unsuited for combat in western Europe and sent some 200 of these fighters to the Soviets, Zemke was one of two Americans who went to Russia to oversee the re-erection of the Tomahawks, to test-fly them, and familiarise Russian pilots with the aircraft. This task completed, he moved to Moscow and, attached to the military attaché's office, studied Luftwaffe reports—Zemke was fluent in German. From Moscow he moved to the Middle East and Africa for similar duties before returning to the United States in the spring of 1942 where he was put in charge of training 120 pilots of the Chinese Nationalist Air Force to fly the Curtiss P-36.

First Thunderbolt group

At this time a few USAAF squadrons were training with the first of the new P-47 Thunderbolts at airfields in the general area of the manufacturers' plant at Farmingdale, Long Island. Many accidents were occurring due to mechanical imperfections as well as pilots' difficulties in mastering such a large and powerful fighter. Zemke, with

Colonel Hubert Zemke (left) established a reputation as a brilliant fighter leader commanding the 56th Fighter Group. Known as the Wolfpack, the 56th was the top-scoring US Eighth Air Force fighter group. Zemke is pictured with three of the Group's aces (from right to left) Capt F. J. Christensen, Lt Col F. S. Gabreski and Lt Col D. Schilling

his penchant for the technical, was a natural choice to command the first Thunderbolt group, which he was given in August. Under his leadership many of the mechanical problems were solved and training proceeded rapidly. Personnel of the 56th Fighter Group sailed for England in January 1943.

Thunderbolts were not available to the Group in England for several weeks as two other USAAF groups in the country were being converted to the type from the Supermarine Spitfire and Lockheed Lightning. The 56th, together with these other units, became operational early in April 1943 but at first the Thunderbolts made a poor showing in combat with the experienced Luftwaffe. Nevertheless, in a surprise attack on an Fw 190 formation flying near Liège on 13 June, Zemke made the second and third kill for his Group. Compared with its main adversaries, the P-47 was slow to accelerate and its rate of climb was poor. On the other hand, it was very fast at high altitude, had a tremendous dive speed and good firepower. Zemke set out to exploit the advantages of the aircraft and develop the best tactics. On his personal aircraft, nicknamed *Moy Tavarish* (Russian for 'My Comrade'), he had the armoured glass removed to save weight and flew with six instead of eight guns. With the availability of drop tanks to extend range, the 56th had one successful engagement after another. On 2 October during a sortie to Emden, Zemke destroyed his fifth enemy aircraft to become the second ace in the Group.

At the end of October 1943 Zemke was ordered to return to the United States to visit aircraft factories and air bases on a morale-boosting tour, but not before destroying his seventh enemy aircraft the day before leaving the 56th's base. He returned to his Group in mid-January and on 11 February claimed the first enemy aeroplane destroyed by strafing for the 56th when a low-level pass was made across Juvincourt airfield. By 14 March, when he was awarded the Distinguished Service Cross by General Spaatz, Zemke had increased his air score to ten. The award was for his actions in leading the 56th FG on

its very successful operations of 11 February and 6 March 1944. Further successes followed, but by the summer of 1944 the long-range Mustang units were seeing most of the action with the Luftwaffe and the P-47s were often diverted to ground attack.

Prisoner of War
Off duty, Zemke followed his love of sport. It was said that he took part in the enlisted men's boxing contest in London by entering as 'Corporal Zemke', a rumour which brought little comment but a chuckle from the Colonel. In August the commander of a neighbouring Lockheed P-38 group was missing in action and the 56th Fighter Group's deputy commander, David Schilling, was offered the vacant command. Schilling declined, but hearing that the P-38 group was about to convert to

Mustangs, Zemke volunteered for the job. First flying a Lightning and then a Mustang, Zemke gained further victories with his new command, the 479th Fighter Group, taking his score to $19\frac{1}{2}$, 17 of which had been achieved with the P-47. (A later reassessment of scores reduced the total to $17\frac{1}{2}$.) A few weeks later after joining the 479th its original commander, Kyle Riddle, returned, having come down in France and evaded capture by the enemy. As Zemke out-ranked him (being a full Colonel), Riddle became his deputy. However, on 30 October Riddle regained his command when Zemke's Mustang had airframe failure in a violent storm and the famed pilot baled out over Germany. It was a long-standing joke between Zemke and Riddle after the war that Riddle had sawn halfway through the wing of Zemke's P-51 in order to get his command back.

Zemke was taken prisoner and after lengthy interrogation was sent to Stalag-Luft I near Barth where he was the senior Allied officer. Zemke ran Stalag-Luft I in much the same efficient way that he ran his fighter groups, organising various activities to keep up the morale of the 9,000 prisoners. When, early in May 1945, the Germans wanted to march the prisoners west, Zemke managed to persuade the German commandant to let selected prisoners take over the guarding of the camp. This was basically for the protection of the prisoners who were liberated by the Russians the day after the German staff departed. Hubert Zemke continued his air force career in the immediate postwar years, retiring from the USAF in 1967.

Above: the 56th FG was the only Eighth Air Force Group to fly the Republic P-47 throughout operations in Europe.
Left: pictured from left to right, Zemke, Christensen, Gabreski and Schilling, the Group's deputy CO, trace the course of a mission.
Right: Zemke on occasion removed two machine guns from his P-47D to lighten it and thus improve the aircraft's performance

Acrobats from Czechoslovakia

The Zlin family of low-wing monoplanes from Czechoslovakia are well-known for their manoeuvrability

A shoe factory in an obscure Czechoslovakian town is an unlikely location for a manufacturer of aeroplanes, but in 1935 the Bata Shoe Company established its aircraft-building subsidiary in Otrokovice, near the city of Zlin (now called Gottwaldov after Czechoslovakia's first Communist premier). Consequently the company was named Zlinská Letecká Akciová Spolecnost, or Zlin Aeroplane Works.

Zlin's first product was the Zlin 12, a low-wing, wood-and-fabric, two-seat trainer powered by a 40hp Persy engine. The efficient little aeroplane won the fuel consumption event at the 1937 International Air Meeting in Cairo, and was placed high in the Oases Circuit air race against competitors with much more powerful engines. A beautiful racing aeroplane followed and then, with the German occupation, Zlin's own design activities came to a halt while the Otrokovice works was forced to manufacture Bücker Bü 181 Bestmann trainers for the Luftwaffe. After the war the Bestmann remained in production as the Zlin C6 and C106 for the Czech air force and as the Zlin 381 for flying clubs.

State nationalisation

Zlin's first original postwar design was the Model 22, a much-modified Bestmann powered by a 75hp Praga engine which entered production in 1947. This three-seater with its slightly-swept wings bore scant resemblance to the German machine. The Zlin 122, a four-seat tourer version, proceeded no further than the prototype stage.

In 1948 two events of great significance to the Zlin company took place. A new Communist government nationalised the company as Czechoslovakia's State Aircraft Industry, and Zlin introduced an all-new, tandem two-seat trainer, the Zlin 26. The Model 26 went into quantity production and remained on the Otrokovice line until 1953, when it was succeeded by the Zlin 126 Trener II, whose swept-back wings and inverted inline 105hp

Walter Mikron engine set the style for all Zlin aerobatic aircraft for a quarter of a century. The Trener was produced for Czech military and State-run civilian flying schools, and also for export to other countries of the Eastern Bloc.

When the improved, all-metal Zlin 226 entered production in 1955 the Czechoslovakian company's name soon became known beyond the Iron Curtain. The 226 was produced in three versions: the Z226B Bohatyr

places went to Czech pilots flying Zlin 226 Akrobat Specials. The great Ladislav Bezak became world champion and was later to use both his superlative skills and the Zlin's versatility to escape from East to West Germany carrying his wife and two children aboard the two-seater, evading some intercepting MiGs *en route* before making good his flight to freedom.

Again at the 1962 World Championships in Hungary, and at Bilbao in Spain two years later, Zlins took top

Below: the Cherokee-like Zlin 42 two-seat sporting monoplane is powered by a 180 hp Avia engine. First flown on 17 October 1967, it has been produced in quantity for private pilots and as a military liaison aircraft

glider tug, Z226T Trener and the Z226A Akrobat, a single-seat version intended for competition aerobatic work. All were powered by the 160 hp Walter Minor 6-III engine. It was at the Lockheed Aerobatic Trophy competition at Coventry, England in 1956 that the West was given a foretaste of the Czech domination of aerobatics which was to last more than a decade. Zlin factory pilot Jiri Blaha was placed second behind the incomparable Leon Biancotto in a standard Trener and astonished spectators with the aircraft's ability to perform flick manoeuvres and knife-edge flight.

The Czechs 'invented' a new aerobatic manoeuvre in their versatile Zlins – *lomcevak* – which starts with an inverted or 'outside' snap roll and ends with the aircraft tumbling end over end, imposing severe strains on airframe and pilot. Roughly translated, *lomcevak* means 'hangover headache', an apt description of the manoeuvre's effect on the pilot.

When the first World Aerobatics Championships were held at Bratislava, Czechoslovakia in 1960, the first four

honours and remained undefeated until the Russians scored a home victory at Moscow in 1966 with the big Yak 18PM which had been developed especially to combat the threat of the Zlins. Although the Yak's abundant power enabled it to perform better in the vertical plane, the Zlin had better snap-rolling qualities and was able to manoeuvre in a smaller aerobatic 'box' than the aircraft from Russia.

Eclipse of the Akrobat

Meanwhile the Otrokovice works had not been idle. While the original Zlin 226s were proving a fair match for contemporary competition, a new version with a slightly extended wing and a retractable undercarriage had been developed. As with earlier models, the Zlin 326 was offered in both two-seat Trener-Master and single-seat Akrobat variants. However, such was the performance of the aircraft that many western aerobatic pilots were more than pleased to get their hands on the basic trainer, which was a far cry from the Tiger Moth and Stampe biplanes on

Opposite top: it was with the all-metal Zlin 226 Akrobat that Czechoslovakia first achieved prominence in postwar international aerobatic competitions. Opposite centre: a refinement of earlier Akrobats, the Zlin 526 was eclipsed by the Pitts Special in the 1970 World Aerobatic Championships. Opposite: the pre-war Zlin 12 trainer was the company's first design

which they had struggled gamely against the Eastern Bloc competition for years.

The new Zlins recaptured their world title at Magdeburg, East Germany in 1968. That contest was an inauspicious occasion, however, for it heralded the arrival of a new and potent newcomer to the competition aerobatics scene – the tiny Pitts Special biplane, which was to oust the Zlin from its pinnacle within a few short years.

By 1970, when the World Aerobatics Championships were held in England, improved Zlin 526s with self-contained constant-speed propellers were standard equipment with all Eastern Bloc countries, except the Soviet Union. Although 35 pilots in the competition flew Zlins of some sort, the Yaks and Pitts Specials prevented them from collecting any honours. It was while practising for the 1970 contest that a Zlin 526A Akrobat flown by the late Neil Williams suffered a mainspar failure in flight. Williams rolled the aircraft until it was inverted, using air pressure to retain the wing in its normal position, and flew back to RAF Hullavington where he rolled the aircraft out of inverted flight just before touching down. He was quite unhurt – a tribute to both his skill and the strength of the Zlin.

The Zlin's heyday seemed to have past, but work was in hand at Otrokovice to improve the basic design further. In February 1971 the prototype Zlin 526AFS flew, powered by a 180hp Avia M137A engine in place of the Walter Minor. The new Akrobat had clipped wings to improve its roll rate, double ailerons instead of the aileron/flap arrangement of earlier models and a 59kg (130lb) weight reduction. The 526AFS was 35 per cent faster in the roll and was able to sustain knife-edge flight for longer than its predecessors. However, neither it nor the 200hp Lycoming-engined Zlin 526L – developed to meet American FAA certification requirements – was able to counter the Pitts' domination at the 1972 championships in Salon-de-

Provence. The current production models of Zlins long-lived aerobat are the 726 and 726K with 180hp and supercharged 210hp Avia engines. In all, some 1,500 Trener/Trener-Master/Akrobats have been delivered.

Sporting-touring aeroplane
While work proceeded on developing training and competition aerobatic aircraft, the Otrokovice factory also flew a prototype sporting/touring aeroplane – the Zlin 42 – on 17 October 1967. The two-seat Zlin 42 and its four-seat counterpart, the Zlin 43, are all-metal, low-wing tricycle undercarriage machines using the same engines as the current 726 models. More than 200 have been manufactured, including some used for the purpose of military liaison.

The eclipse of the Akrobat from world-class competition spurred development of an entirely new design. The Zlin 50L, which first flew in July 1975, is typical of modern aerobatic design thinking. It is small, with a 260hp Lycoming engine conferring a high power-to-weight ratio for vertical manoeuvres and features a fully-inverted fuel and oil system and symmetrical wing for outside figures. Its constant-speed propeller can serve as an airbrake and a comfortable, carefully-designed seat makes 'g' loads more bearable for the pilot.

Despite the Zlin 50L's newness, the Czech pilots came second in the team event and third in men's individual at the 1976 World Championships at Kiev in Russia. The little Zlin demonstrated remarkable controllability at low airspeeds and was easily able to manage multiple vertical and outside snap rolls, triple vertical 8s and 'square' manoeuvres. Not surprisingly, when the 1978 championships were held at Ceské Budejovice in Southern Bohemia, Czech Ivan Tucek took the world title flying a Zlin 50L which is rapidly becoming standard equipment in the Eastern Bloc, just like its illustrious forerunners.

The diminutive Zlin 50L bids fair to emulate the success of its predecessors in the world aerobatic arena. Manoeuvrability at all speeds and altitudes is particularly noteworthy

The Illustrated Encyclopedia of

AVIATION

INDEX

How to use this Index

Numbers in **bold** type (**1**) refer to volume numbers. Numbers in *italics* (*47*) refer to illustrations. Numbers in Roman (607) refer to entries on a subject. Thus:

Alison, Major John R. **1**: *47*, **6**: 607

indicates that an illustration of Major John R. Alison appears in Volume **1**, page *47*, with a text entry in Volume **6**, page 607.

Page references volume by volume

A

C

D

M

N

O

P

R

T

W